Pokémon

Unofficial Card Collector's Guide

Mike Searle & Tom Slizewski

Publications International, Ltd.

Mike Searle and Tom Slizewski are the lead editors at *InQuest Gamer,* the leading monthly magazine for collectible card games. They have written about card games and collectible cards for over ten years for publications including *Wargame Collector's Guide* and *Wizard: The Comics Magazine*. Mike spends most of his days trying to build the perfect Pikachu deck. Tom has given up on Pikachu and swears his Squirtle Speed Deck can take on anyone, although maybe not Charizard, Gyarados, or Nidoking.

Louis Weber, CEO
Publications International, Ltd.
7373 North Cicero Avenue
Lincolnwood, Illinois 60712

Manufactured in U.S.A.

8 7 6 5 4 3 2 1

ISBN: 0-7853-4292-3

Table of Contents

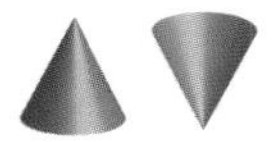

THE POKÉMON PHENOMENON

Pokémon has grossed a remarkable $7 billion worldwide. Pikachu, Charmander, and the rest of the 151 characters are becoming as recognizable as Mickey Mouse, Donald Duck, and the whole Disney cast. More than 100,000 video game cartridges sell every week in America. If you had any doubt that Pokémon is the biggest franchise heading into the new millennium, then you probably haven't been trying to collect sold-out Jungle and Fossil cards for the last few months.

JAPANESE TAKE-OUT

So how did this whole Pokémon phenomenon start? You have to travel back in time to 1996 and the release of Nintendo's "Pocket Monsters" Game Boy video game in Japan. Pocket Monsters (what they call Pokémon in Japan) exploded on the scene with addictively cute characters, created by Japanese animé star Satoshi Tajiri, and an ingeniously interactive game system. The idea is simple: You're a trainer trying to track down rare pokémon, and the only way to collect them all is to hook your Game Boy up with your friend's and trade. But it isn't as simple as just buying the game and trading—there are two games, Pokémon Red and Pokémon Blue. The game plays the same for both, but each has different pokémon to discover. Pokémon became a collecting frenzy, and, 15 million cartridges later, it has become a cultural icon, as important to the Japanese as *Star Wars* is to American culture.

With the tremendous success of the video game, Pokémon spread into other media. In almost no time, the cartoon shot up in the standings to earn recognition as the highest-rated children's television show ever in Japan. Comic books followed and flew off the newsstands, and the Pokémon music CD sold over a million copies. Not to be outdone, the Pokémon card game debuted and sold over 400 million cards, setting in motion the quality and collectibility of a game that would soon be translated to America in force.

This is not a fluke or quick fad. Poké mania has continued for an almost unbelievable 50 straight months in Japan, and, with more than 1,000 different licensed Pokémon products being sold, there's still a wealth of characters and cards to come our way.

COMING TO AMERICA

Who said lightning never strikes twice? Pikachu and his pokémon friends are on pace to duplicate the Japanese phenomenon in the United States. The cartoon hit television screens in September 1998 and immediately hooked kids on the adventures of pokémon trainer Ash. In the first season's 52 episodes, Ash befriended Pikachu and collected pokémon of all shapes and sizes, from Bulbasaur to Charmander to Squirtle, on his way to the Pokémon League Championship. Animated giant robotic pokémon, ghosts in haunted houses, and ninja trainers have all grabbed an audience that brought the show to number one for youngsters and number three for teenagers. With a second season of 52 episodes being translated from Japanese, and the impact of the *Pokémon: The First Movie* motion picture in November 1999, expect the momentum to continue well into the twenty-first century.

And that's not even counting the power of the video games. Just as in Japan, the Pokémon Blue and Pokémon Red Game Boy

Top 5 Most Valuable Pokémon Cards

(All are holofoil versions.)

1. Charizard
2. Blastoise
3. Raichu
4. Venusaur
5. Alakazam

cartridges have electrified kids in America from the start, and the games have kept coming. The summer of 1998 saw the release of Pokémon Pinball, with its vibrating flippers and a catalog of 150 Pokémon characters. July 1999 saw the launch of Nintendo 64's Pokémon Snap—you can now take snapshots of your favorite pokémon in the wild. Fall 1999 brought Pokémon Pikachu Yellow, the first new Game Boy cartridge since Red and Blue, with Pikachu as your sidekick. Then there is the promise of Nintendo 64's Pokémon Stadium, which will pit pokémon against pokémon in battles, just as the cartoon does.

All this craziness continues with Wizards of the Coast's collectible card game. All 151 pokémon—including Pikachu, Meowth, and Gastly—can be found in the card sets, with a select few—including Charizard, Scyther, and Ditto—getting special holographic foil pictures on their cards. These "holofoils" are rare and are included in less than half the packs sold. Even rarer are special promotional cards that are given away in magazines or at select events. The most recent examples were the four pokémon cards given away at the pokémon movie. Cards featuring the villain of the show, Mewtwo, were handed out with the purchase of a theater ticket, as were cards of the flying Dragonite, the electrifying Electabuzz, and Ash's little pal, Pikachu.

Of course, you can't always find the cards. They're so hot that printers run around the clock to manufacture the cards, and second editions arrive almost at the same time as first editions. Wizards of the Coast still can't keep up with the demand. A standard 11-card booster pack should retail for $3.29, but the scarcity has pushed the price up to $6, even $11, a pack. With collectors' desires continuing to rise after having collected the Basic set and the Jungle expansion, Fossil, the expansion released in October 1999, was sold out almost immediately after its release. A complete Fossil set now goes for around $500.

The card-collecting frenzy has fired up a full-fledged mall tour of the Pokémon League to feed fans' interest. Upwards of 10,000 kids have stood in lines at their local malls to buy, trade, and play Pokémon. The tour was organized by Nintendo, and it traveled around the country in the spring and summer of 1999. Fans hoping to find their favorite characters found not only the cards but also poké balls full of pokémon memorabilia of all shapes and sizes. Also, there was the Poké-mobile, a Volkswagen Bug painted and sculpted to look like a four-wheeled version of Pikachu.

The Pokémon League provides an arena for fans who want to play the game on a regular basis in a social environment against competitors their age. Participants earn points toward a trainer badge for joining various pokémon-related activities, whether they be collecting certain pokémon cards or battling other pokémon trainers, and they get unique promotional cards available only through the League. For example, in January 2000 the League releases a card for the 151st pokémon, Mew. Originally part of the Japanese Fossil set, Mew, in addition to being the rarest pokémon in the pokémon world, owns one of the most powerful pokémon powers in the card game—a nice bonus card for League members. Leagues run for six weeks, and registration fees vary, though they are reasonably priced. The League has been very successful; in Toys 'R Us stores alone, 20,000 fans signed up in the first week.

The cards were the final catalyst to catapulting pokémon into the American consciousness. With TV, video games, and cards exposing fans to a wave of pokémon products, the avalanche of merchandise rumbled into the United States and rolled over the competition during the holiday season. We saw plush stuffed animals of Pikachu and Snorlax, plastic figurines of Gengar and Rattata, Poliwhirl and Eevee micro play sets, Bulbasaur and Clefairy stamps, Blastoise and Mewtwo bouncy balls, electronic Meowth and Charmander toys, Ash and Misty lunch boxes—you name it, some sort of gift idea has hit the stores. We've even seen Charizard temporary tattoos, Squirtle squirt rings, and Mew finger puppets. With the merchandise trend still growing, the pokémon invasion has conquered America and opened up a huge collector's market for the hottest item since Beanie Babies.

CARD CRAZE

"Catch 'em all" isn't just the "catch" phrase of the cartoon, it's also the motto of card collectors nationwide. Those seeking to track down all the cards would have had an easier time if they had started back in December 1998, when the first edition of the Basic set was released. The Basic set includes 102 cards and half the existing pokémon. Of those pokémon, the rare holofoil characters, such as Charizard, Blastoise, and Mewtwo, command a much higher price than their common or uncommon brethren, and even other nonfoil rares. Also, there are first edition and second edition cards. Think of first edition as a first printing and second edition as a second printing. Naturally, first edition cards are seen as the originals and rack up a higher price. Sometimes there are even minor differences in the editions, as was the case with Machamp. This stage 2 pokemon only appeared in the first edition and in one of the preconstructed decks.

After the Basic set was released in December 1998, Jungle, the first expansion, was released in June 1999. This set concentrated on the grass pokémon—some of the less popular pokémon—and so didn't generate the same amount of activity the Basic set and Fossil, the third set, did. Still, Jungle introduced a new concept for pokémon cards—rare and holofoil versions of the same card. In the Japanese set, a rare card such as Kangaskhan was only a holofoil. In the American release, however, there was a separate rare Kangaskhan and a holofoil version. Thus, the Japanese Jungle set has 48 cards, while the U.S. version, with its double amount of rares, has 64 cards.

Mew is the 151st pokémon. It is a very rare creature in the wild and as a card. It was part of the Japanese Fossil set, but for the English editions of that set, Mew was pulled from the deck. The card was translated into English, but it is only available to members of the Pokémon Player's League.

By the time Fossil hit, Pokémon fever had erupted to a raging pitch in the United States, and October brought sold-out claims from stores across the country. The same rarity scheme was applied to the American Fossil set—16 commons, 16 uncommons, and double the rares—except, instead of 64 cards in American Fossil, there are only 62. Mew, the ever popular 151st pokémon, was removed from the set when it was translated from the Japanese cards to English. It is a promo card for the Pokémon League.

Of course, fans of the game know that all these cards already exist over in Japan and have for three years. Currently, only the Basic, Jungle, and Fossil cards have been translated into English, but there are over 400 more cards awaiting translation. The 64-card Team Rocket set is due out in spring 2000. It's based around the pokémon cloned by the villains of Team Rocket. These pokémon aren't nice, and so their name is preceded by the word "bad" to distinguish them from the nicer versions.

Before Team Rocket, a new basic set will be hitting store shelves. As for the other Japanese sets, nothing is definite yet, but you can guarantee pokémon popularity will bring them to the States sooner than later. What other sets exist in Japan? Gym Leaders is the big one. Six fixed decks—decks that have the same cards every time you buy one—of Gym Leaders come with 64 cards each, and then there are

Gym Leaders Expansion 1 and Gym Leaders Expansion 2, 96 cards and 98 cards, respectively. More than likely, we'll see these in the summer or fall of 2000.

Beyond that are the tougher-to-find vending machine cards. As the name suggests, these cards are sold in game stores in Japan, but they are bought from vending machines, just like we'd buy gum balls or soda pop. To nab them all, you have to collect all three vending machine sets (108 cards) and a special Southern Islands theme set (18 cards). It's unknown at this time whether these cards will ever be translated into English.

Finally, Japan has a slew of promo cards. Whether from big events, magazine inserts, or tournament giveaways, these promo cards were scattered across Japan in different media. Finding them all would be a big, nearly impossible job. Fortunately, the job got considerably easier with the release of the Promo Card Intro Pack, which gathers 82 pokémon cards into a single set. Much like the vending machine cards, it's a safe bet we won't see the promo cards in English, at least not for a while.

MORAL BACKLASH

It's no wonder that with Pokémon thrust into the limelight, eventually there would be some negative backlash against the game. Despite praise for Pokémon downplaying violence—pokémon are knocked out, not killed—some groups across the country are up in arms about an addictive game that has so seized their children. A church in Colorado Springs, Colorado, claims the obsessive nature of the game is detrimental to kids, who lose interest in family activities, and can cause children to become desensitized to violence. Other complaints have been that pokémon sport horns—associating them with the devil—and that the game, and its Web sites, are linked to other "demonic" games, such as Magic: The Gathering and Dungeons & Dragons.

Not all adults think that way, however. In September 1999, the National Parenting Center, an independent testing group of parents and educators who single out products of quality and merit, awarded Pokémon their Seal of Approval. They stated that "Pokémon is a compelling game that involves strategy, creative thinking and a dash of luck. We haven't seen young boys so excited about a game of this nature in a long time."

GOTTA OWN 'EM ALL

Though the cards are often hard to find, it's easy to catch the Pokémon collecting bug. Hundreds of thousands of kids—of all ages and from around the world—have caught it and are eager to assemble an entire set. Here are things to keep in mind during your quest to get all those cards.

Collectibility is affected by three main things. First among these is "rarity." Rarity refers to how many of a certain card are in circulation. Except for special promotional cards, all English-language Pokémon cards are one of four rarities:

Common. Marked with a black dot on the bottom right-hand corner of the card. These are the easiest to get and usually not worth much. You'll get seven commons in every booster pack.

Uncommon. Marked with a black diamond on the bottom right-hand corner of the card. These are slightly more difficult to get but are still plentiful. You'll get three uncommons in every booster pack.

Rare. Marked with a black star on the bottom right-hand corner of the card. These are difficult to find and therefore of great interest to collectors. You'll only get one rare in every booster pack.

Ultra Rare (Holofoil). These cards are also marked with a black star, but they stand out from other rares because they are printed on a thin layer of shiny foil. On average, you will get one holofoil in every three packs.

After rarity, a card's price is affected by what edition it came from. The first cards printed in each expansion have a small first edition symbol below the picture. Only a limited number of first edition cards are printed. After that number is reached, all subsequent cards are second edition. They are identical to earlier printed cards, except they don't have the first edition symbol. (The only exception was the result of a printing error in Jungle that had the nonholofoil Electrode with its Basic set picture. This was later corrected.)

> **Top 5 Most Powerful Pokémon**
>
> 1. Hitmonchan
> 2. Scyther
> 3. Ditto
> 4. Chansey
> 5. Alakazam

After rarity and edition, a card's power in the game also affects its collectibility. Though it's estimated that less than half of Pokémon card collectors play the game, powerful cards are in higher demand by people who do play competitively. Since both players and collectors want the powerful cards, the increased demand translates into higher values.

Playing a minor factor in a card's collectibility is the card's "star" appeal. That's why many trainer cards lag in value; collectors favor pokémon. Cards of Pikachu and Charizard command more because of their fame. For Pikachu it's not much, but Charizard is the most valuable card.

CARD ANATOMY

A. Pokémon Type: Basic, Stage 1, or Stage 2

B. Pokémon Name: Abra to Zapdos

C. Hit Points: How much damage a pokémon can take before being knocked out. You have to equal this number, not exceed it.

D. Pokémon Type: There are seven types of pokémon: grass, water, fighting, electric, fire, psychic, and colorless.

E. Picture Box

F. Edition Symbol: It will say first edition here if it is; if it isn't, this space will be blank.

G. Measurements: The pokémon's physical statistics.

H. Expansion Symbol: Blank for the Basic edition, a paw print for Jungle, a skeletal foot for Fossil, an R for Team Rocket, a target with the word "Gym" for Gym Leaders.

I. Pokémon Power: Most pokémon don't have one, but if it does there will be writing here explaining what the power does.

J. Resistance: If there's an energy symbol here, it will be followed by a minus sign and a number (usually 30). This means that this pokémon takes minus that number of damage from any pokémon of this color.

K. Basic Attack: This is the lower energy attack this pokémon can perform. Some can only perform one kind of attack, but most have two.

L. Advanced Attack: This is the higher energy attack this pokémon can perform. Not all pokémon have a second attack; Ratatta, for example, has only one.

M. Damage: This number is the amount of damage this attack deals.

N. Weakness: If there's an energy symbol present here, it means that this pokémon will

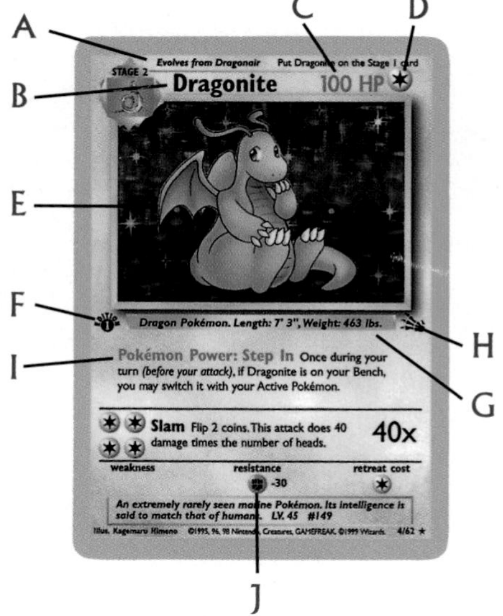

take double damage from any pokémon that are this color.

O. **Retreat Cost:** This is the amount of energy this pokémon must spend to move from your active area back to your bench. Costs can range from none to as high as three.

P. **Art Credit:** This is the artist who illustrated the card.

Q. **Copyright:** This is required for legal reasons and is a good way to make sure a card is authentic and not a counterfeit.

R. **Card Number:** The first number is the card's number in the set it's from; the second is the total number of cards in the set. For example, 52/64 would mean that this is card number 52 from a set that contains 64 cards.

S. **Rarity Symbol:** There is a circle for commons, a diamond for uncommons, or a star for rares.

T. **Flavor Text:** This gives you a few facts about the pokémon. At the end of that information is the level number and then the pokémon number.

GOOD GRADES

Collectors interested in eventually selling their collections must pay careful attention to the physical condition of their cards. A single crease in a card will lower its value by half or more!

There's a big market for buying and selling collectible card game cards (generally called CCGs). Since your idea of "good" may be different from someone looking to buy your cards, a precise grading scale has been adopted by card collectors. Note that all prices in this guide assume Near Mint or better condition. From best to worst the scale looks like this:

MINT A card that is, or looks, brand new. There can be no scratches, bends, or other wear for a card to be in this condition.

NEAR MINT (NM) This is a card that looks new. If you look closer, though, you may find a few hairline scratches and other minor wear marks. More than three such minor marks and your card's condition changes to Very Fine.

VERY FINE (VF) More than three minor marks but still in good shape overall. A card in this condition has no creases, water damage, or obvious imperfections. This is the lowest grade most collectors will accept. Values start to go down fast if a card's condition is lower than VF.

FINE Worn edges and immediately obvious imperfections, usually around the corners, mark a card as Fine. Players of the game who are not collectors first will usually still be interested in Fine grade cards.

VERY GOOD (VG) If a card shows white fraying around the edges on both sides when laid flat but otherwise has no water damage or creases, it is considered Very Good. Heavily played cards not kept in card sleeves quickly become this condition.

GOOD Heavily played cards with all four edges worn or frayed, slight creases, and even minor spots of smudged ink are called "good" even though they can look pretty rough.

FAIR A card so worn that it is considered "marked" for tournament play. "Marked" means that it has significant enough wear marks that the owner could tell what the card is even while looking at its back. All cards that are written on are considered no better than Fair.

POOR Water damage, a tear of any size, a crease down the middle, a deep scratch—this type of damage puts a card into the Poor category. Poor cards have no resale value.

CARE AND FEEDING OF YOUR POKÉMON CARDS

You can see from the careful grading scale that condition is important to collectors. That's why you always want to protect your cards as much as possible. That doesn't mean not playing with them, though! Pokémon cards are meant to be fun first, not treated like art treasures and locked in a safe.

To allow you to play with your cards while keeping wear to a minimum, you should spend a few dollars on card sleeves. The leading maker of card sleeves is a company called

Rembrandt. It sells sleeves under the brand name Ultra Pro Deck Protectors. Each sleeve holds one card, though it can hold two. The sleeves are legal for tournament play.

If you plan on just collecting and not playing, individual card sleeves are not for you. Check out Ultra Pro's line of card protector pages. Each plastic page has 9 pockets and holds 18 cards (9 on each side). The pages fit in standard three-ring notebooks. For your collectible cards, it's important to get good-quality card protector pages that are acid free, offer protection from ultraviolet light, and will hold your cards without damage for years. You may be able to find cheaper plastic pages, but these may damage your cards. They are probably not archival quality, and they will deteriorate over time and ruin your cards.

FAKE CARDS

It's hard to believe, but it's true; there are thousands of fake pokémon cards on the market. After the game enjoyed huge sales and certain rare cards began to command big money, several overseas companies began to print counterfeit cards.

These fakes are worthless, so be aware of the following:

1. Real cards are sold only in foil boosters, two-player starter sets, or preconstructed theme decks. Counterfeits are often sold in "sandwich" bags or plastic booster packs that are not foil.
2. Real cards are the same size and are on thick card stock. Counterfeits are on flimsier paper and are often not the same size as authentic cards. Stack the cards tightly and make sure they form a tight, even deck.
3. Fake cards often have slightly fuzzy or washed-out artwork. Since fakes are often computer scans of real cards, the makers have difficulty matching the bright, deep colors of the authentic ones.
4. Real cards all have the copyright: 1995, 96, 98, 99 Nintendo, Creatures, GAMEFREAK. ©1999 Wizards. Note: Earlier printed cards do not have the 99 before Nintendo. Counterfeiters often don't copy the copyright line so that if they're caught they can claim they didn't know they were copying copyrighted material.

Top 5 Favorite Pokémon Web Sites

The Pojo at http://www.pojo.com/
Want pokémon information overload? Look no further. This site is run by the most knowledgeable people in the game.

The Wizards of the Coast Offical Pokémon Website at http://www.wizards.com/pokemon/
This is the place to get official news on errata, card lists, and so forth. One of the best places for beginners to come and grasp the basics or just get some common questions answered.

The Pokémon Center at http://pokec.com/index2.html
This site's primary focus is the Pokémon video game, but it makes the list because it's an awesome fan resource presented in a fun way.

Edo's Pokémon Page at http://www.geocities.com/TimesSquare/Alley/2247/Poke.htm
This site is not for beginners, as there's a learning curve in navigating around it. But there is treasure here, including scans of most cards and lots of info on things like ultra-rare promotional cards.

Pokémon World at http://www.pokemon.com/pokedex/
Professional site that lets you look up each pokémon individually and see the cards in all their colorful glory.

HOW TO USE THIS GUIDE

This book is the most complete collection of information available for Pokémon card collectors anywhere. You will find detailed listings for every English-language Pokémon card printed. There's also preview information about future Pokémon cards that are currently only available in Japanese.

To get maximum use of this book, here's a guide to the listings:

Power Rating: How good this card is in the

game on a scale of 1 to 5; 1 is lousy and 5 is awesome. This is the number before the name.

Pokémon Name

Collectibility Rating: How much in demand this card is on a scale of 1 to 5; 1 is "not very" and 5 is "everybody wants it." This is the number to the right of the name.

Set: What set the card was released with. These are Basic, Jungle, Fossil, Team Rocket, Gym Leaders Preconstructed Decks, Gym Leaders 1, and Gym Leaders 2.

Evolution: What this pokémon evolves from and what it evolves into.

Card Number: Each Pokémon card has a number from 1 to however many cards are in the set it was released in. Japanese cards are not numbered like this and instead feature the pokémon's number, from 1 to 151 (see listing on page 94).

Rarity: How likely you are to find this card. Common, Uncommon, Rare, Rare (Holofoil), and most difficult: Ultra Rare.

English First Edition Price: The price range the first edition of this card is being sold for at stores around the United States.

English Second Edition Price: The price range the second edition of this card is being sold for at stores around the United States.

Japanese Price: The price range the Japanese-language edition of this card is being sold for at stores around the United States.

Description: A brief biography of the pocket monster or a special note about its play value or collectibility.

THE PRICE IS RIGHT

The prices listed in this book were derived by surveying dealers across the United States and cross-referencing our findings with the leading collectible card game price guides, both print and electronic. We list a price range because values fluctuate and vary by regions of the country. The range is what 90 percent of the cards of that type have sold for.

BUY, BUY

Demand has been so high for pokémon cards that Wizards of the Coast has been unable to print enough—especially the first four to six weeks after a set is released. Get your cards early by placing an order with your local card shop.

Your local store should be your first choice on where to buy cards. These stores usually sell singles, often sponsor trade or game nights, and are places to meet other collectors. If you don't have a card store near you, check the Internet. Search for "pokemon cards retail" on your computer, and you'll get many matches. Also, visit our favorite Web sites (see page 10), and follow the links to online retailers.

There are also auction sites online for bidding on Pokémon cards and collections. Type "pokemon" in the search field, and you'll find many matches.

WHEELING AND DEALING

A big part of the fun of collecting is bartering with other collectors. It's a way to complete your collection without spending a fortune. There's one golden rule when trading: Only make trades you want to make! If you're new to trading, here are a couple of ground rules:

Commons for commons is a fair trade.

Uncommons for uncommons is usually a fair trade. The exception is Double Colorless Energy—it's worth at least two other uncommons.

Rares for rares is tricky. Look at the prices in this guide, and judge such trades accordingly.

Consider how much you want the card that's being traded. Trades don't always have to be even. If you have three alakazams and only need a nidoking to finish your collection, make the trade. The other person may get the better deal, but you'll get a complete set! And it's hard to put a value on that.

You're collecting cards because it's fun. Your hobby should be fun first, and business should be a distant second. You can't put a price on fun.

Now go out and round up those pokémon!

Basic Set

102 First Edition Cards; 101 Second (Unlimited) Edition Cards

Abra

Set: Basic
Evolution: Into Kadabra
Card Number: 43
Rarity: Common
English 1st Edition Price: $.50–$1
English 2nd Edition Price: $.25–$.50
Japanese Price: $.50–$.75

Unlike almost every other pokémon, Abra hates to fight. It lives in the wilds of the forest and uses its telepathic ability to hide from other pokémon and pokémon trainers. During the rare times it gets caught and is forced to battle, it will use its teleport ability to escape the first chance it gets.

Alakazam

Set: Basic
Evolution: From Kadabra
Card Number: 1
Rarity: Rare (Holofoil)
English 1st Edition Price: $25–$40
English 2nd Edition Price: $16–$22
Japanese Price: $15–$20

Hundreds of times smarter than any human who has ever lived, Alakazam is among the toughest pokémon in existence. Its super intelligence gives it the same abilities as its lower evolutions, Abra and Kadabra, but also allows it to learn advanced fighting moves.

Arcanine

Set: Basic
Evolution: From Growlithe
Card Number: 23
Rarity: Uncommon
English 1st Edition Price: $2.50–$4.50
English 2nd Edition Price: $1.25–$2.50
Japanese Price: $1.25–$2.50

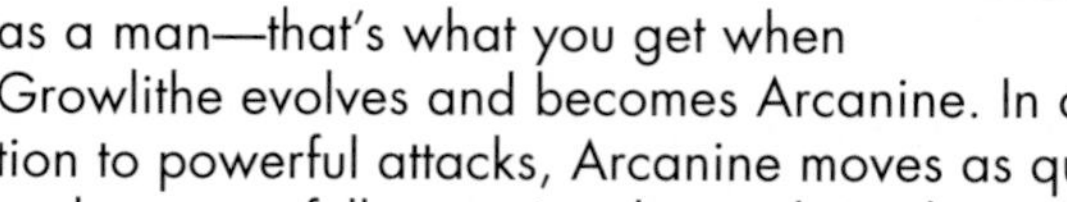

A dog with fur made out of fire and as tall as a man—that's what you get when Growlithe evolves and becomes Arcanine. In addition to powerful attacks, Arcanine moves as quickly and as gracefully as a jungle cat, but it has a big dog's bite. Arcanines are particularly popular at Blaine's Gym.

Beedrill

Set: Basic
Evolution: From Kakuna
Card Number: 17
Rarity: Rare
English 1st Edition Price: $14–$18
English 2nd Edition Price: $8–$12
Japanese Price: $7–$10

With three stingers, Beedrill is one bee you don't want to bug. Though its earlier stages—Weedle and Kakuna—are weak, this final stage packs a powerful one, two, three punch. And it's hard to get away from, as Beedrill flies very quickly even though it's the size of an average dog!

Blastoise

Set: Basic
Evolution: From Wartortle
Card Number: 2
Rarity: Rare (Holofoil)
English 1st Edition Price: $40–$55
English 2nd Edition Price: $16–$24
Japanese Price: $15–$22

Among the five most sought-after poké-mon, Blastoise's special power is among the best in the game. It uses its twin water blasters to pulverize its oppo-nents, all the while letting its trainer play as many water cards as he or she wants. Decks that use Blas-toise's special ability to win games are called "Rain Dance" decks and are very common at tournaments.

Bulbasaur

Set: Basic
Evolution: Into Ivysaur
Card Number: 44
Rarity: Common
English 1st Edition Price: $.50–$1
English 2nd Edition Price: $.25–$.50
Japanese Price: $.50–$.75

A mixture of grass, poison, and seed, Bulbasaur must live with a strange plant bulb on its back. This bulb starts to grow as the pokémon evolves, and the bulb eventually blooms fully when Bul-basaur reaches its most advanced stage, Venusaur. While generally shy, Bulbasaur will fight to defend its territory.

Caterpie

Set: Basic
Card Number: 45
Evolution: Into Metapod
Rarity: Common
English 1st Edition Price: $.50–$1
English 2nd Edition Price: $.25–$.50
Japanese Price: $.50–$.75

Like a caterpillar, Caterpie can cling to things like trees and buildings. The webs it shoots slow down pokémon attacking it, buying time to tie them up or get itself away. Because Caterpie evolves into the worthless Metapod, it's not very popular with pokémon trainers or collectors.

Chansey

Set: Basic
Evolution: None
Card Number: 3
Rarity: Rare (Holofoil)
English 1st Edition Price: $26–$38
English 2nd Edition Price: $14–$18
Japanese Price: $12–$16

The always cheerful Chansey is difficult to catch and not well suited for fighting. In battle it usually just hides its face and protects its eggs. When charged up enough, it can launch a devastating attack, but it takes an equal amount of damage itself. Chansey is a tournament favorite and one of the five most sought-after cards.

Charizard

Set: Basic
Evolution: From Charmeleon
Card Number: 4
Rarity: Rare (Holofoil)
English 1st Edition Price: $65–$100
English 2nd Edition Price: $35–$45
Japanese Price: $35–$45

Very similar to a dragon, Charizard has wings and is able to shoot super-hot flames out of its mouth. These flames are so hot they melt everything in its path, even rocks! This super ability has made it the second most popular pocket monster; only Pikachu is more popular. Charizard is also one of the five most sought-after cards in the game and the single most valuable pokémon to collectors.

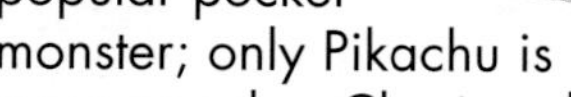

Charmander

Set: Basic
Evolution: Into Charmeleon
Card Number: 46
Rarity: Common
English 1st Edition Price: $.50–$1
English 2nd Edition Price: $.25–$.50
Japanese Price: $.50–$.75

Though it looks like a miniature orange Barney, Charmander is a lot more dangerous since it's filled with fire. Sometimes this fire leaks out and can be seen as a small flame on the tip of its tail. It feels right at home around volcanoes and lava, but it is vulnerable to water attacks.

Charmeleon

Set: Basic
Evolution: From Charmander/Into Charizard
Card Number: 24
Rarity: Uncommon
English 1st Edition Price: $2.50–$4.50
English 2nd Edition Price: $1.25–$2.50
Japanese Price: $1.25–$2.50

Not only is Charmeleon nearly twice as big as the cuddly Charmander, it's also three times as ferocious. When Charmander evolves into this beast, the tiny flame on its tail grows to the size of a torch and a single horn pops out of the back of its head. Charmeleon can attack with its fiery tail or use its super-sharp claws.

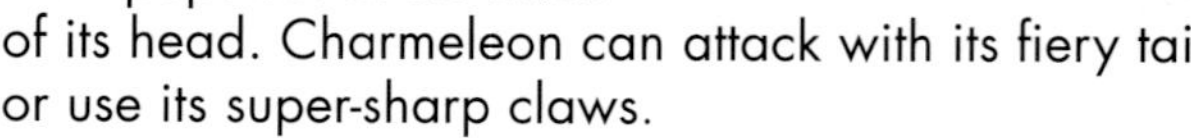

Clefairy

Set: Basic
Evolution: Into Clefable
Card Number: 5
Rarity: Rare (Holofoil)
English 1st Edition Price: $22–$34
English 2nd Edition Price: $14–$20
Japanese Price: $12–$18

Extremely shy and bashful, Clefairy can only be found in a very few places in the wild. A clefairy was originally going to be the star of the game and cartoon, but a last-minute decision resulted in Ash getting Pikachu instead. That's probably for the best, as Clefairy would hate the attention.

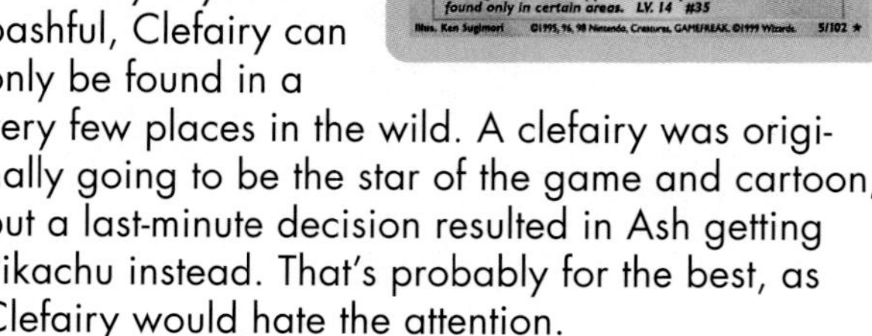

Dewgong

Set: Basic
Evolution: From Seel
Card Number: 25
Rarity: Uncommon
English 1st Edition Price: $2.50–$4.50
English 2nd Edition Price: $1.25–$2.50
Japanese Price: $1.25–$2.50

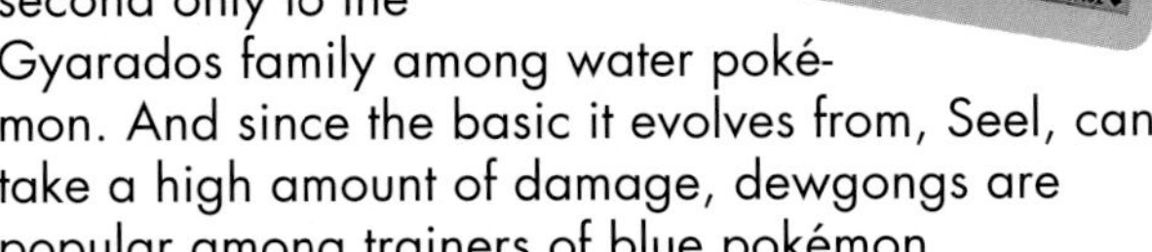

Equally at home in ice cold or warm water, Dewgong packs a punch second only to the Gyarados family among water pokémon. And since the basic it evolves from, Seel, can take a high amount of damage, dewgongs are popular among trainers of blue pokémon.

Diglett

Set: Basic
Evolution: Into Dugtrio
Card Number: 47
Rarity: Common
English 1st Edition Price: $.50–$1
English 2nd Edition Price: $.25–$.50
Japanese Price: $.50–$.75

Though it spends most of its time burrowing just a few feet underground, Diglett will come to the surface if its territory is threatened or to join the occasional pokémon battle. It hates to be removed from its home habitat and is among the most fragile of basic pokémon.

Doduo

Set: Basic
Evolution: Into Dodrio
Card Number: 48
Rarity: Common
English 1st Edition Price: $.50–$1
English 2nd Edition Price: $.25–$.50
Japanese Price: $.50–$.75

Think of the Road Runner of cartoon fame with an additional head, and you'll have an accurate picture of how Doduo battles: It uses its speed to its best advantage. Though technically a bird, Doduo can't fly, but, like all bird pokémon in the game, it can stand up well to fighting attacks.

Dragonair

Set: Basic
Evolution: From Dratini
Card Number: 18
Rarity: Rare
English 1st Edition Price: $14–$18
English 2nd Edition Price: $6–$10
Japanese Price: $5–$8

You have to figure that a pokémon that can change the weather whenever it wants to is going to be tough to beat. And you'd be right. Dragonair is a vicious fighter that does not have to use any single energy type to make its devastating energy-stealing attack. With the right draw, it can use its attack on turn two. Ouch.

Dratini

Set: Basic
Evolution: Into Dragonair
Card Number: 24
Rarity: Uncommon
English 1st Edition Price: $2–$4
English 2nd Edition Price: $1–$2
Japanese Price: $1–$2

For a long time people thought the eel-like Dratini was unique, that only a single one like it existed. But after several more were discovered in the Safari Zone, it was realized that these little dragons are what dragonairs evolve from. Note that though dratinis spend most of their time in the water, they are not water pokémon.

Drowzee

Set: Basic
Evolution: Into Hypno
Card Number: 49
Rarity: Common
English 1st Edition Price: $.50–$1
English 2nd Edition Price: $.25–$.50
Japanese Price: $.50–$.75

There's a good reason this pokémon is called Drowzee—its specialty is putting the pokémon it's fighting to sleep. Once its rival is asleep, Drowzee attacks its dreams, and in this way often knocks out even the toughest, most high-level opponent. Its major weakness is other drowzees.

Dugtrio

Set: Basic
Evolution: From Diglett
Card Number: 19
Rarity: Rare
English 1st Edition Price: $14–$18
English 2nd Edition Price: $6–$10
Japanese Price: $5–$8

Three digletts banded together can spell big trouble, as their combined earth-burrowing ability can be used to make the ground shake violently. This deals damage not only to the pokémon they're currently fighting but to every pokémon in the immediate vicinity, including those on Dugtrio's side. Make sure you know how to get to your closest pokémon center if you plan on using these guys.

Electabuzz

Set: Basic
Evolution: None
Card Number: 20
Rarity: Rare
English 1st Edition Price: $15–$20
English 2nd Edition Price: $7–$11
Japanese Price: $5–$9

Electabuzz can usually be found near strong sources of electricity. It can absorb large amounts of electrical power, store it, and then release it during battles. Not only does this zap its opponent, it often knocks out the power where it is, making it easy to locate—just look for all the blacked-out houses.

Electrode

Set: Basic
Evolution: From Voltorb
Card Number: 21
Rarity: Rare
English 1st Edition Price: $14–$18
English 2nd Edition Price: $6–$10
Japanese Price: $5–$8

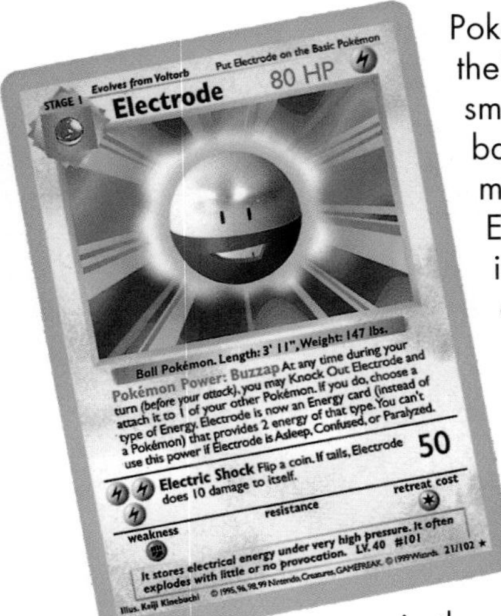

Pokémon trainers keep their pokémon inside small red-and-white balls when the pokémon are not battling. Electrode uses this to its advantage by appearing as a standard poké ball. But it's not a standard poké ball, it's actually a floating bomb that can explode suddenly, knocking itself out in the process.

Farfetch'd

Set: Basic
Evolution: None
Card Number: 27
Rarity: Uncommon
English 1st Edition Price: $2.50–$4.50
English 2nd Edition Price: $1.25–$2.50
Japanese Price: $1.25–$2.50

It looks and quacks like a duck, but Farfetch'd is a much tougher fighter than any regular duck. It uses twigs and onion sprigs as weapons and has one of the most potent first-turn attacks in the game. Since it's resistant to fighting and is colorless, Farfetch'd is found in many tournament decks.

Gastly

Set: Basic
Evolution: Into Haunter
Card Number: 50
Rarity: Common
English 1st Edition Price: $.50–$1
English 2nd Edition Price: $.25–$.50
Japanese Price: $.50–$.75

As a poison ghost pokémon, Gastly is very hard to see. When you do catch a glimpse of it, Gastly appears as a large ball of gas with two smaller white balls for eyes and vampirelike teeth. In game terms, Gastly is among the worst, having the lowest hit points and a wimpy first-turn attack that has only a 25 percent chance of fully working.

Growlithe

Set: Basic
Evolution: Into Arcanine
Card Number: 28
Rarity: Uncommon
English 1st Edition Price: $2.50–$4.50
English 2nd Edition Price: $1.25–$2.50
Japanese Price: $1.25–$2.50

A fierce young dog that will steadfastly protect its home turf, Growlithe is found in only three areas in pokémon land. In the cartoon, it requires a fire stone to evolve into the much-feared Arcanine. That's not necessary in the card game, but, in both the game and the cartoon, it absolutely hates water.

Gyarados

Set: Basic
Evolution: From Magikarp
Card Number: 6
Rarity: Rare (Holofoil)
English 1st Edition Price: $24–$32
English 2nd Edition Price: $14–$20
Japanese Price: $5–$8

Third heaviest and second longest of all pokémon, Gyarados is also among the five most powerful. It can wipe out whole villages when angry and can knock out many basic pokémon with just one attack. Luckily for us, it is very rare and usually keeps to itself. Also, it has to evolve from the super-weak pokémon Magikarp.

Haunter

Set: Basic
Evolution: From Gastly
Card Number: 29
Rarity: Uncommon
English 1st Edition Price: $2.50–$4.50
English 2nd Edition Price: $1.25–$2.50
Japanese Price: $1.25–$2.50

You can't hide from Haunter; this ghost-type pokémon can go anywhere and is difficult to hit with physical punches. But that doesn't make it good in game terms. That's because, just like the Gastly it evolves from, Haunter requires a lot of luck for its attacks to work. Its big damage attack only has a 25 percent chance of working, and Haunter's low hit points means it won't likely be around for a repeat attack.

Hitmonchan

Set: Rare
Evolution: None
Card Number: 7
Rarity: Rare (Holofoil)
English 1st Edition Price: $26–$34
English 2nd Edition Price: $12–$16
Japanese Price: $12–$16

Named after martial arts star Jackie Chan, this fighting powerhouse is among the best pokémon in the game. Why? Because as a basic it can be played quickly, do a lot of damage, take a lot of damage, and many of its foes are weak to fighting. Decks that use many fast fighters like Hitmonchan are called "Haymaker" decks in tournament play.

Ivysaur

Set: Basic
Evolution: From Bulbasaur/Into Venusaur
Card Number: 30
Rarity: Uncommon
English 1st Edition Price: $2.50–$4.50
English 2nd Edition Price: $1.25–$2.50
Japanese Price: $1.25–$2.50

As the evolved version of Bulbasaur, Ivysaur is an up-powered version of that pokémon. Its main physical difference is that the plant on its back is starting to bloom and its skin gains spots. It also becomes poisonous. If another pokémon inhales the powder Ivysaur releases when it attacks, that pokémon becomes poisoned and quickly loses hit points.

Jynx

Set: Basic
Evolution: None
Card Number: 31
Rarity: Uncommon
English 1st Edition Price: $2.50–$4.50
English 2nd Edition Price: $1.25–$2.50
Japanese Price: $1.25–$2.50

Though Jynx tries to appear human, it isn't. It's actually an unusual combination of psychic energy and ice. It prefers to use its super-powerful mind to launch mental attacks, though it will also use its hands to physically attack pokémon that get too close. Oddly, it is particularly vulnerable to mental attacks.

Kadabra

Set: Basic
Evolution: From Abra/Into Alakazam
Card Number: 32
Rarity: Uncommon
English 1st Edition Price: $2.50–$4.50
English 2nd Edition Price: $1.25–$2.50
Japanese Price: $1.25–$2.50

Talk about a headache. Kadabra causes others to get them just by being near. Kadabra is physically weak and relies on its mind exclusively when attacking. This may sound like a weakness, but since its mental attack is the strongest of any purple pokémon, it isn't really. Its relatively low hit points aren't a great concern either, since it evolves into the damage-removing Alakazam.

Kakuna

Set: Basic
Evolution: From Weedle/Into Beedrill
Card Number: 33
Rarity: Uncommon
English 1st Edition Price: $2.50–$4.50
English 2nd Edition Price: $1.25–$2.50
Japanese Price: $1.25–$2.50

As the name implies, Kakuna is a kind of cocoon that a weedle hides in so it can emerge as the powerful Beedrill. While in this immobile hard-cocoon stage, Kakuna can only attack by emitting a poisonous powder that's harmful to other pokémon who get too close. Kakunas hate fire.

Koffing

Set: Basic
Evolution: Into Weezing
Card Number: 52
Rarity: Common
English 1st Edition Price: $.50–$1
English 2nd Edition Price: $.25–$.50
Japanese Price: $.50–$.75

Think of a big purple balloon full of many nasty, foul-smelling, poisonous gases, and you have an accurate picture of what Koffing looks like. And just like a balloon, Koffing can accidentally get too full and pop in a big messy explosion. It doesn't explode as often as Electrode or Voltorb, but good pokémon trainers are always aware of the possibility.

Machamp

Set: Basic
Evolution: From Machoke
Card Number: 8
Rarity: Rare (Holofoil)
English 1st Edition Price: $8–$12
English 2nd Edition Price: Only in 1st Edition
Japanese Price: $10–$15

What's stronger than a nearly 300-pound body builder? A nearly 300-pound body builder with two sets of arms! Strong doesn't always translate into super-powerful in game terms, though; Machamp takes too much energy to use its strength effectively. Machamp was only in the first edition of the Basic set, not the second (unlimited) edition. Machamp, however, was a fixed card in the two-player starter set.

Machoke

Set: Basic
Evolution: From Machop/Into Machamp
Card Number: 34
Rarity: Uncommon
English 1st Edition Price: $2.50–$4.50
English 2nd Edition Price: $1.25–$2.50
Japanese Price: $1.25–$2.50

The middle stage of the muscle man evolution looks like a blue Arnold Schwarzenegger with three bony green ribs on its head. All that muscle-building has resulted in Machoke's body becoming unstable—so unstable that it has to wear a special belt to coordinate its movements.

Machop

Set: Basic
Evolution: Into Machoke
Card Number: 52
Rarity: Common
English 1st Edition Price: $.50–$1
English 2nd Edition Price: $.25–$.50
Japanese Price: $.50–$.75

Constantly working out to increase its muscle size, Machop may be small but it's a good fighter. It is seen in nearly all fast decks, since it's one of the few pokémon who can deal 20 points of damage on the first turn of the game and have a enough hit points to withstand anything an opponent may attack back with.

Magikarp

Set: Basic
Evolution: Into Gyarados
Card Number: 35
Rarity: Uncommon
English 1st Edition Price: $2.50–$4.50
English 2nd Edition Price: $1.25–$2.50
Japanese Price: $1.25–$2.50

The second weakest pokémon—only Porygon is weaker—Magikarp exists for only one reason: to evolve into Gyarados. Before evolving, it is just a big fish with wimpy attacks and the lowest hit points of any pokémon in the game. Since it can be knocked out with one good attack, Magikarp should never be in play for more than one turn before evolving.

Magmar

Set: Basic
Evolution: None
Card Number: 36
Rarity: Uncommon
English 1st Edition Price: $2.50–$4.50
English 2nd Edition Price: $1.25–$2.50
Japanese Price: $1.25–$2.50

Appearing like a monster made of lava, Magmar is at home only in and around fire. Naturally it hates water, but it also doesn't get along well with pokémon of other colors. Since Magmar does not evolve into a more powerful form, top pokémon trainers don't much care for it. Talk about being a black sheep.

Magnemite

Set: Basic
Evolution: Into Magneton
Card Number: 53
Rarity: Common
English 1st Edition Price: $.50–$1
English 2nd Edition Price: $.25–$.50
Japanese Price: $.50–$.75

Made of everyday objects such as screws and magnets, this cute pokémon can fly around using a strange form of antigravity. Be careful though; appearances can be deceiving. It may look like it's screwed together carefully, but it can explode at any time to deliver a nasty attack. Experienced pokémon trainers always use a defender before exploding their magnemites.

Magneton

Set: Basic
Evolution: From Magnemite
Card Number: 9
Rarity: Rare (Holofoil)
English 1st Edition Price: $28–$36
English 2nd Edition Price: $12–$18
Japanese Price: $10–$16

Proof that a whole is not necessarily stronger than its individual parts, Magneton is three magnemites magnetically stuck together. This banding triples their basic attack but otherwise provides few benefits and several drawbacks. Why you'd ever want to evolve a perfectly good magnemite for this is as puzzling as Magneton's origin, which has stumped scientists. There does seem to be a link, however, between when it appears and the weather on the sun.

Metapod

Set: Basic
Evolution: From Caterpie/ Into Butterfree
Card Number: 54
Rarity: Common
English 1st Edition Price: $.50–$1
English 2nd Edition Price: $.25–$.50
Japanese Price: $.50–$.75

Metapod looks and acts like a really big green banana. But you can't eat it. Metapod is not a fruit; it's a hibernation stage for the caterpillarlike Caterpie to evolve into the butterflylike Butterfree. The stages of this evolution are all cute, but none are powerful in game terms and are best avoided.

Mewtwo

Set: Basic
Evolution: None
Card Number: 10
Rarity: Rare (Holofoil)
English 1st Edition Price: $30–$38
English 2nd Edition Price: $12–$18
Japanese Price: $12–$18

There is technically only one Mewtwo. It is the star of the pokémon feature film, *Pokémon: The First Movie.* It was created for evil purposes by researchers using advanced biological techniques, such as cloning, to defeat all the other pokémon. In game terms, it does not live up to this reputation and is not particularly useful.

Nidoking

Set: Basic
Evolution: From Nidorino
Card Number: 11
Rarity: Rare (Holofoil)
English 1st Edition Price: $25–$35
English 2nd Edition Price: $12–$18
Japanese Price: $8–$14

Looking much like a small stegosaurus, Nidoking is a big armored lizard with bony plates, spikes, and horns all over its body. Where all other pokémon are "its," rather than male or female, Nidoking starts out as a male and its counterpart, Nidoqueen, starts out as a female. Nidoking's advanced attack is among the most energy efficient in the game.

Nidoran (male)

Set: Basic
Evolution: Into Nidorino
Card Number: 55
Rarity: Common
English 1st Edition Price: $.50–$1
English 2nd Edition Price: $.25–$.50
Japanese Price: $.50–$.75

Nidoran looks like a big floppy-eared puppy—except it has spiky horns down the ridge of its back. It's known as the all-or-nothing pokémon, because its sole attack works only half the time. It does a lot of damage for the energy required, but Nidoran's low hit points mean it won't be around to try more than twice before being knocked out.

Nidorino

Set: Basic
Evolution: From Nidoran/Into Nidoking
Card Number: 37
Rarity: Uncommon
English 1st Edition Price: $2.50–$4.50
English 2nd Edition Price: $1.25–$2.50
Japanese Price: $1.25–$2.50

When a nidoran puppy grows up, it takes the shape of a nidorino: a small, spiky, pink rhinoceros. Like a rhino, a nidorino charges with its head held low in an attempt to impale its foe on its horn. And, as if that weren't bad enough, the horn has poison on it, making its attack extra powerful.

Ninetales

Set: Basic
Evolution: From Vulpix
Card Number: 12
Rarity: Rare (Holofoil)
English 1st Edition Price: $24–$32
English 2nd Edition Price: $11–$17
Japanese Price: $8–$14

As the name implies, this pokémon has nine tails. Ninetales does not exist in the wild. The only way a pokémon trainer can get one is by nurturing and building up a Vulpix. It's worth the effort though, as Ninetales is the most deadly pokémon in the game, dealing more damage over two turns than even the dreaded Charizard.

Onix

Set: Basic
Evolution: None
Card Number: 56
Rarity: Common
English 1st Edition Price: $.50–$1
English 2nd Edition Price: $.25–$.50
Japanese Price: $.50–$.75

The longest of all pokémon, Onix appears as a string of small, multi-faceted boulders. The front rock has a face and a single horn sticking straight up out of its head. Though it looks like it's made of ordinary dark granite, the stone Onix is composed of is as hard as any gem. Its biggest drawback is that all that weight makes it move very s—l—o—w—l—y.

Pidgeotto

Set: Basic
Evolution: From Pidgey
Card Number: 22
Rarity: Rare
English 1st Edition Price: $10–$16
English 2nd Edition Price: $5–$8
Japanese Price: $4–$8

Much like a rooster, Pidgeotto is aggressive and doesn't often back down from a fight. The problem is, like a rooster, it is mostly attitude. It is too small and too weak to inflict much damage, so it usually loses fights. Since pidgeottos are very common in the wild, pokémon trainers have their pokémon battle them often to gain experience.

Pidgey

Set: Basic
Evolution: Into Pidgeotto
Card Number: 57
Rarity: Common
English 1st Edition Price: $.50–$1
English 2nd Edition Price: $.25–$.50
Japanese Price: $.50–$.75

Like its namesake, Pidgey looks like and has all the power and fearsomeness of a pigeon. It is also as common as a pigeon. Not a good combination for pokémon trainers trying to win against fiery lizards and huge sea monsters. Because it flies, Pidgey's good at dodging fighting attacks. Other than that, though, there is nothing to recommend it.

Pikachu

Set: Basic
Evolution: Into Raichu
Card Number: 58
Rarity: Common
English 1st Edition Price: $.50–$1
English 2nd Edition Price: $.25–$.50
Japanese Price: $.50–$.75

Yellow and mouse-like, pikachus—particularly Ash's Pikachu—are the best-known and most-loved pokémon of all. They naturally generate electricity, which they discharge at their opponents when battling. Pokémon trainers are cautious about keeping too many pikachus at the same time, as several of them together can generate dangerous thunderbolts.

Poliwag

Set: Basic
Evolution: Into Poliwhirl
Card Number: 59
Rarity: Common
English 1st Edition Price: $.50–$1
English 2nd Edition Price: $.25–$.50
Japanese Price: $.50–$.75

Poliwags are babies who can't stand up on their own very well. They resemble giant tadpoles and are usually found swimming in clean, clear water. They can go on land but much prefer to stay wet until they evolve. Their hypnotic markings are designed to mesmerize their opponents, and this strategy works well against all but the smartest pokémon.

Poliwhirl

Set: Basic
Evolution: From Poliwag/Into Poliwrath
Card Number: 38
Rarity: Uncommon
English 1st Edition Price: $2.50–$4.50
English 2nd Edition Price: $1.25–$2.50
Japanese Price: $1.25–$2.50

The "teenage" stage of the poli-evolution has no problem walking on land or swimming through seas. It uses both its brain and its brawn in fights. If it can get close enough, Poliwhirl will punch like a boxer. If it can't get in close, it will use its mental ability to make the pokémon it is fighting against forget how to fight.

Poliwrath

Set: Basic
Evolution: From Poliwhirl
Card Number: 13
Rarity: Rare (Holofoil)
English 1st Edition Price: $28–$38
English 2nd Edition Price: $12–$18
Japanese Price: $10–$16

Once it is all grown up, the adult poli becomes an awesome fighter. And while Poliwrath moves considerably slower than its prior evolution, it gains great amounts of strength and endurance. Though water-based, Poliwrath's combined strength and endurance allows it to stand up to fire pokémon with no ill effects. It hates bug and poison pokémon from the green family, though.

Ponyta

Set: Basic
Evolution: Into Rapidash
Card Number: 60
Rarity: Common
English 1st Edition Price: $.50–$1
English 2nd Edition Price: $.25–$.50
Japanese Price: $.50–$.75

A pony made of pure white heat, Ponyta moves extremely quickly and uses its hooves, speed, and fiery tail to deliver devastating attacks. While this may sound like a perfect combination, it isn't. Its attacks require a lot of energy to deliver, and, like most fire-based pokémon, Ponyta hates water.

Porygon

Set: Basic
Evolution: None
Card Number: 39
Rarity: Uncommon
English 1st Edition Price: $2.50–$4.50
English 2nd Edition Price: $1.25–$2.50
Japanese Price: $1.25–$2.50

Without a doubt, this is the weakest pokémon in the game. That may be because Porygon doesn't actually exist! It lives inside a computer. And while that may be great for moving through the cyber jungle, in the real world Porygon is just a long string of computer code. And even the weakest pokémon can beat up on that.

Raichu

Set: Basic
Evolution: From Pikachu
Card Number: 14
Rarity: Rare (Holofoil)
English 1st Edition Price: $30–$45
English 2nd Edition Price: $15–$20
Japanese Price: $15–$20

It's Pikachu on steroids; the evolved form of the yellow mouse wields even more electrical power. So much, in fact, that it has to be careful to always be grounded so it doesn't shock itself. But high voltage isn't its only trick. In addition, it possesses mouselike speed and reflexes—making it extremely difficult for its opponents to damage it.

Raticate

Set: Basic
Evolution: From Rattata
Card Number: 40
Rarity: Uncommon
English 1st Edition Price: $2.50–$4.50
English 2nd Edition Price: $1.25–$2.50
Japanese Price: $1.25–$2.50

Among the most common of all pokémon, Raticate uses its whiskers to move stealthily and to maintain its balance. It attacks with its sharp buckteeth, which can deliver a painful bite to even the toughest pokémon. Since it doesn't have much of a brain, it shrugs off psychic attacks. But since it's so small, it takes extra damage when physically punched or kicked.

Rattata

Set: Basic
Evolution: Into Raticate
Card Number: 61
Rarity: Common
English 1st Edition Price: $.50–$1
English 2nd Edition Price: $.25–$.50
Japanese Price: $.50–$.75

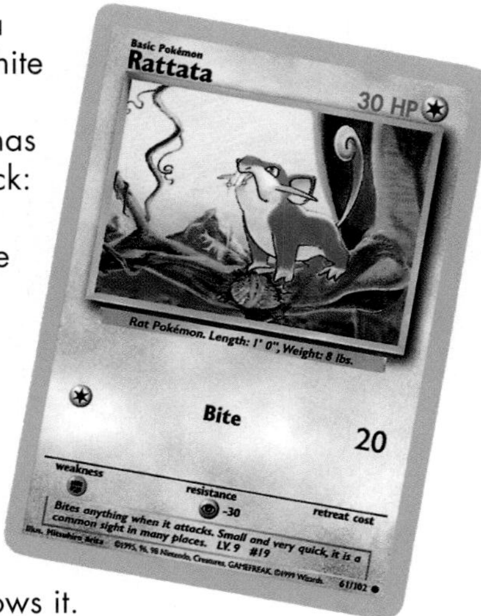

Looking much like a purple rat with a white belly and big buck-teeth, Rattata only has one method of attack: bite and run. Because, while it is the fastest in the game, it is just too small and fragile to fight any other way. Many pokémon that specialize in fighting can KO Rattata with one hit. And Rattata knows it.

Sandshrew

Set: Basic
Evolution: Into Sandslash
Card Number: 63
Rarity: Common
English 1st Edition Price: $.50–$1
English 2nd Edition Price: $.25–$.50
Japanese Price: $.50–$.75

You are not likely to see this rodent in the wild, since Sandshrew lives in the ground and only goes topside when it's hungry. In the Pokémon Red video game, you'll never find it. In the card game, it's plentiful. Since it only takes 40 hit points, you still won't see it much in play.

Seel

Set: Basic
Evolution: Into Dewgong
Card Number: 41
Rarity: Common
English 1st Edition Price: $.50–$1
English 2nd Edition Price: $.25–$.50
Japanese Price: $.50–$.75

An arctic dweller that's happiest chasing and eating fish, Seel always does the same thing when in a pokémon duel. Namely, it tries to smash its head into its opponent's head. This works to its advantage, because Seel's head is extremely hard and has a single horn that makes this maneuver particularly painful to most other pokémon.

Squirtle

Set: Basic
Evolution: Into Wartortle
Card Number: 63
Rarity: Common
English 1st Edition Price: $.50–$1
English 2nd Edition Price: $.25–$.50
Japanese Price: $.50–$.75

Second in cuteness only to Pikachu, Squirtle is a little baby turtle that can shoot streams of bubbles at its enemies. This isn't a powerful attack, however, and it uses this strategy mostly as a diversion so it can run away. Squirtle is vulnerable when young, but it becomes extremely tough as it gets older and evolves.

Starmie

Set: Basic
Evolution: From Staryu
Card Number: 64
Rarity: Common
English 1st Edition Price: $.50–$1
English 2nd Edition Price: $.25–$.50
Japanese Price: $.50–$.75

Starmie is a gigantic starfish-like aquatic creature that mostly wants to be left alone. It isn't left alone much, however, because in the center of each Starmie is a shiny valuable-looking rock that many people like. Because of its amazing healing ability, Starmie can take a long time to beat. Since it doesn't have much offense, however, it's usually just a matter of time before it loses.

Staryu

Set: Basic
Evolution: Into Starmie
Card Number: 65
Rarity: Common
English 1st Edition Price: $.50–$1
English 2nd Edition Price: $.25–$.50
Japanese Price: $.50–$.75

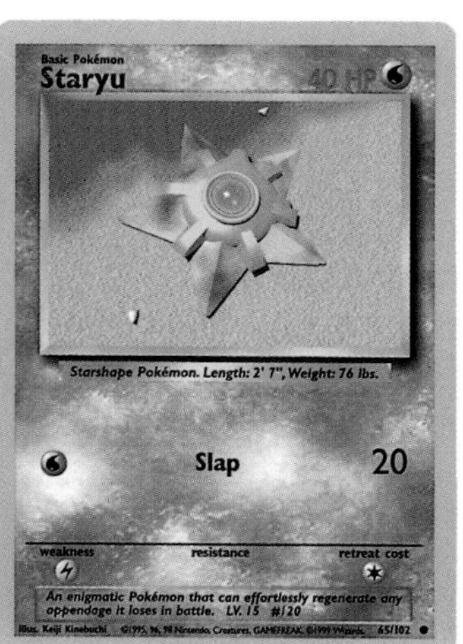

It doesn't look intelligent, but Staryu has a fairly advanced brain and limited mental powers. Like the starfish it resembles, Staryu can regrow a limb should it ever lose one. If you divide a Staryu, it is unknown whether both parts will continue to grow. We don't suggest testing it out with your cards!

2

Tangela

Set: Basic
Evolution: None
Card Number: 66
Rarity: Common
English 1st Edition Price: $.50–$1
English 2nd Edition Price: $.25–$.50
Japanese Price: $.50–$.75

Maybe because it looks like a big ball of green-and-white spaghetti, Tangela is one of the most shy pokémon and will not normally engage in a duel. It should be approached with extreme caution; both its attacks have the potential for effects beyond just a reduction in hit points.

5

Venusaur

Set: Basic
Evolution: From Ivysaur
Card Number: 15
Rarity: Rare (Holofoil)
English 1st Edition Price: $30–$45
English 2nd Edition Price: $15–$20
Japanese Price: $15–$20

The final stage of what began as Bulbasaur, Venusaur has a fully blooming plant on its back and looks imposing even standing still. It has the ability to move energy from any of your pokémon to any other of your pokémon. This is among the five best abilities in the game, and many tournament decks are based around using this power.

Voltorb

Set: Basic
Evolution: Into Electrode
Card Number: 67
Rarity: Common
English 1st Edition Price: $.50–$1
English 2nd Edition Price: $.25–$.50
Japanese Price: $.50–$.75

Using its disguise of looking just like a big poké ball, Voltorb seeks to ambush its opponents. It is never found in the wild; instead it is found wherever electricity is being produced. Before it evolves into Electrode, it's very fragile, particularly against pokémon that specialize in fighting.

Vulpix

Set: Basic
Evolution: Into Ninetales
Card Number: 68
Rarity: Common
English 1st Edition Price: $.50–$1
English 2nd Edition Price: $.25–$.50
Japanese Price: $.50–$.75

Think of this as the first step toward a Ninetales: Raising a Vulpix is the only way to get one of those much sought-after pokémon. That's not to say that Vulpix is easy to catch; this orange catlike creature is actually quite hard to find in the wild. Though it has nine tails even at this stage, it hasn't learned any good attacks and is quite useless.

Wartortle

Set: Basic
Evolution: From Squirtle/Into Blastoise
Card Number: 42
Rarity: Uncommon
English 1st Edition Price: $2.50–$4.50
English 2nd Edition Price: $1.25–$2.50
Japanese Price: $1.25–$2.50

A big turtle that uses its ears like rudders, Wartortle seeks to lure its opponents into the water where it can use its superior speed to swim circles around them. Then, when its opponent least expects it, it will lock its jaws around some part of its enemy's anatomy. Wartortle is good in its own right, but it evolves into the powerful Blastoise.

Weedle

Set: Basic
Evolution: Into Kakuna
Card Number: 69
Rarity: Common
English 1st Edition Price: $.50–$1
English 2nd Edition Price: $.25–$.50
Japanese Price: $.50–$.75

Large, yellow, and fuzzy, Weedle is found almost exclusively living in trees in the forest. It has something on its head that looks like a birthday party hat. It's not! It's a poisonous stinger that inflicts enough damage to knock out the weakest pokémon in only one turn. This is particularly dangerous on the first turn.

Zapdos

Set: Basic
Evolution: None
Card Number: 16
Rarity: Rare (Holofoil)
English 1st Edition Price: $25–$38
English 2nd Edition Price: $15–$22
Japanese Price: $15–$22

Imagine a lightning storm that follows you wherever you go. That's what Zapdos does. A monstrous bird that comes out of the sky unannounced and lets loose with a fireworks display of electrical attacks, it has no known vulnerabilities and loves to eat electrodes before launching its lethal attacks. If you encounter a trainer who has a Zapdos in his or her stable, proceed cautiously.

Trainer Cards

Bill

Set: Basic
Card Number: 91
Rarity: Common
English 1st Edition Price: $.50–$1.50
English 2nd Edition Price: $.25–$.75
Japanese Price: $.50–$.75

Ash's friend helps you go through your deck faster, giving you a better chance of getting the cards you need quickly.

Clefairy Doll

Set: Basic
Card Number: 70
Rarity: Rare
English 1st Edition Price: $8–$14
English 2nd Edition Price: $4–$6
Japanese Price: $4–$6

It looks like a Clefairy pokémon, but it's just a toy used to lure other trainers closer so you can challenge them.

5

Computer Search

Set: Basic
Card Number: 71
Rarity: Rare
English 1st Edition Price: $8–$14
English 2nd Edition Price: $4–$6
Japanese Price: $4–$6

In real life there's no better way to find something than using a computer, and the same holds true for pokémon trainers.

Defender

Set: Basic
Card Number: 80
Rarity: Uncommon
English 1st Edition Price: $2.50–$4.50
English 2nd Edition Price: $1.25–$2.50
Japanese Price: $1.25–$2.50

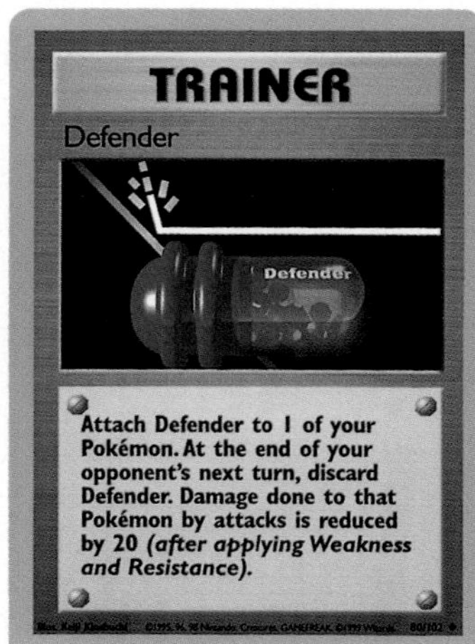

Give your pokémon one of these, and it temporarily gets a force field around it that protects it from harm. But be careful; this power wears out in just one turn.

Devolution Spray

Set: Basic
Card Number: 72
Rarity: Rare
English 1st Edition Price: $6–$10
English 2nd Edition Price: $3–$5
Japanese Price: $3–$5

A single squirt of this liquid will cause any poké-mon to revert to its weaker ver-sion. This is great for when the bigger ones get out of hand and start misbehaving.

Energy Removal

Set: Basic
Card Number: 92
Rarity: Common
English 1st Edition Price: $.50–$1
English 2nd Edition Price: $.25–$.50
Japanese Price: $.50–$.75

Without a constant stream of energy, pokémon can't launch attacks. Enemy trainers play this card to take your energy away.

Energy Retrieval

Set: Basic
Card Number: 81
Rarity: Uncommon
English 1st Edition Price: $2.50–$4.50
English 2nd Edition Price: $1.25–$2.50
Japanese Price: $1.25–$2.50

As a counter to trainers that take away a pokémon's energy, you can play this card to get it back.

Full Heal

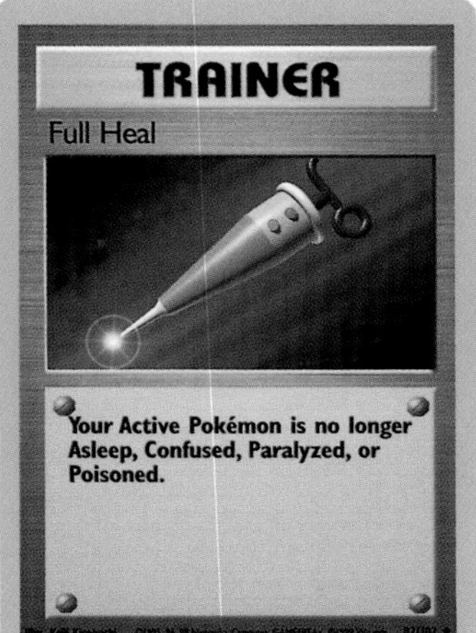

Set: Basic
Card Number: 82
Rarity: Uncommon
English 1st Edition Price: $2.50–$4.50
English 2nd Edition Price: $1.25–$2.50
Japanese Price: $1.25–$2.50

Feed your pokémon one of these, and its ailments disappear. It still has its damage but shakes off the effects of any special attacks.

Imposter Professor Oak

Set: Basic
Card Number: 73
Rarity: Rare
English 1st Edition Price: $7–$12
English 2nd Edition Price: $4–$6
Japanese Price: $4–$6

He looks like the man who knows the most about pokémon. But he's not; this guy is an impostor hired by Team Rocket to look like Professor Oak.

Gust of Wind

Set: Basic
Card Number: 93
Rarity: Common
English 1st Edition Price: $.50–$1
English 2nd Edition Price: $.25–$.50
Japanese Price: $.50–$.75

All it takes is an unexpected puff of air for one of your opponent's poké-mon to be blown forward to where the fight-ing is taking place.

Item Finder

Set: Basic
Card Number: 74
Rarity: Rare
English 1st Edition Price: $7–$12
English 2nd Edition Price: $4–$6
Japanese Price: $4–$6

Sometimes even pokémon train-ers lose a valuable item. When you use this card, you can find it among the cards you've already played.

Lass

Set: Basic
Card Number: 75
Rarity: Rare
English 1st Edition Price: \$7–\$12
English 2nd Edition Price: \$3–\$5
Japanese Price: \$3–\$5

She looks like any regular girl who just wants to watch what's going on, but this Lass can quickly become your friend. After you use all your trainers, play her and your opponent will lose all of his or hers.

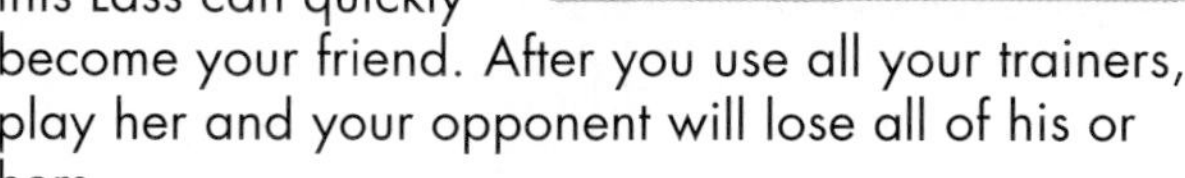

Maintenance

Set: Basic
Card Number: 83
Rarity: Uncommon
English 1st Edition Price: \$2–\$4
English 2nd Edition Price: \$1–\$2
Japanese Price: \$1–\$2

Like a car or a bicycle, you have to stay on top of maintenance to keep a high level of pokémon training ability.

PlusPower

Set: Basic
Card Number: 84
Rarity: Uncommon
English 1st Edition Price: \$2.50–\$4.50
English 2nd Edition Price: \$1.25–\$2.50
Japanese Price: \$1.25–\$2.50

Give your pokémon one of these, and it will do ten more damage the next time it attacks. That may sound wimpy, but it's often the difference between knocking out a big opponent and having it retreat and heal.

Pokédex

Set: Basic
Card Number: 87
Rarity: Uncommon
English 1st Edition Price: \$2.50–\$4.50
English 2nd Edition Price: \$1.25–\$2.50
Japanese Price: \$1.25–\$2.50

Professor Oak invented this electronic gizmo to catalog and record all the characteristics of any pokémon it gets near. Ash almost always carries his wherever he goes.

Pokémon Breeder

Set: Basic
Card Number: 76
Rarity: Rare
English 1st Edition Price: $8–$14
English 2nd Edition Price: $4–$6
Japanese Price: $4–$6

Not everyone is happy being a trainer. The more scientifically-oriented study pokémon and breed them to get more powerful versions.

Pokémon Center

Set: Basic
Card Number: 85
Rarity: Uncommon
English 1st Edition Price: $2.50–$4.50
English 2nd Edition Price: $1.25–$2.50
Japanese Price: $1.25–$2.50

Every major town has one of these hospitals that welcome all trainers to check in their pokémon so they can be fully healed. Visiting these is always on Ash's agenda when he gets to a new town.

Pokémon Flute

Set: Basic
Card Number: 86
Rarity: Uncommon
English 1st Edition Price: $2.50–$4.50
English 2nd Edition Price: $1.25–$2.50
Japanese Price: $1.25–$2.50

The tune of this musical instrument makes certain pokémon dance—they can't help themselves. Experienced trainers know this and use it to catch the shy ones.

Pokémon Trader

Set: Basic
Card Number: 77
Rarity: Rare
English 1st Edition Price: $8–$14
English 2nd Edition Price: $4–$6.50
Japanese Price: $4–$6.50

Just like you do with the cards, in pokémon land there are people who trade the actual pocket monsters. But, no, Ash will never make a trade with you for Pikachu, no matter how many charizards you offer.

Potion

Set: Basic
Card Number: 94
Rarity: Common
English 1st Edition Price: $.50–$1
English 2nd Edition Price: $.25–$.50
Japanese Price: $.50–$.75

These vials of medicine are used by trainers to heal their pokémon during duels. You can buy as many as you can afford at the supply stores located in the larger cities.

Professor Oak

Set: Basic
Card Number: 88
Rarity: Uncommon
English 1st Edition Price: $2.50–$4.50
English 2nd Edition Price: $1.25–$2.50
Japanese Price: $1.25–$2.50

Ash's neighbor and the man who knows the most about all manner of pokémon, Professor Oak gave Pikachu to Ash and continues to help him on his quest to be the top trainer.

Revive

Set: Basic
Card Number: 89
Rarity: Uncommon
English 1st Edition Price: $2–$4
English 2nd Edition Price: $1–$2
Japanese Price: $1–$2

Pokémon rarely get permanently hurt during fights, but they do faint once they've taken too much damage. This trainer lets you wake them up—but at a big penalty.

Scoop Up

Set: Basic
Card Number: 78
Rarity: Rare
English 1st Edition Price: $7–$12
English 2nd Edition Price: $3–$5
Japanese Price: $3–$5

When a situation looks bad for you, sometimes all you can do is grab your pokémon and run. This trainer lets you do that.

Super Energy Removal

Set: Basic
Card Number: 79
Rarity: Rare
English 1st Edition Price: $8–$14
English 2nd Edition Price: $4–$6
Japanese Price: $4–$6

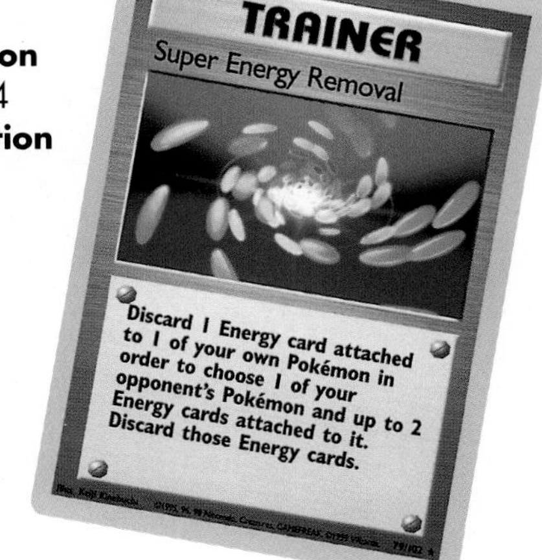

This is the most feared trainer from the Basic set. It robs big pokémon of the huge amounts of energy they need to launch their powerful attacks. Nearly every tournament-level deck has several of these.

Switch

Set: Basic
Card Number: 95
Rarity: Common
English 1st Edition Price: $.50–$1
English 2nd Edition Price: $.25–$.50
Japanese Price: $.50–$.75

If you're playing with the advanced evolutions, you'll want four (the maximum legal number) of this trainer in your deck. That's because big pokémon are expensive to retreat and often get stuck up front. This trainer gets them back to your bench for no energy cost.

Super Potion

Set: Basic
Card Number: 90
Rarity: Uncommon
English 1st Edition Price: $2.50–$4.50
English 2nd Edition Price: $1.25–$2.50
Japanese Price: $1.25–$2.50

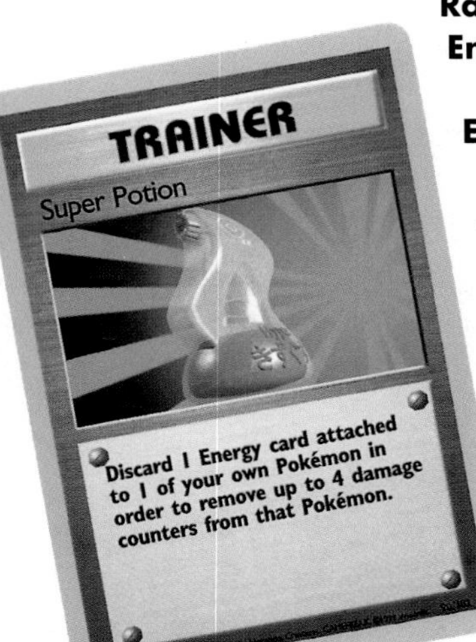

This is the perfect drink for your pokémon that are about to get knocked out. One swig of this and your pokémon gets back 40 hit points, which is usually enough to keep him around for at least one more turn, and often more.

Double Colorless Energy

Set: Basic
Card Number: 96
Rarity: Uncommon
English 1st Edition Price: $4.50–$7
English 2nd Edition Price: $2–$3.50
Japanese Price: $2–$3.50

There's a reason this card is by far the most valuable uncommon—speed. Draw two of these in your opening hand, and you'll quickly be launching big attacks. Even the energy-intensive Charizard needs just two of these to use its 100-point Fire Spin.

Basic Energy

Set: Basic
Card Numbers: 97–102
Rarity: Common
English 1st Edition Price: $.50–$1
English 2nd Edition Price: $.25–$.50
Japanese Price: $.50–$.75

Jungle Expansion

64 First Edition Cards; 64 Second (Unlimited) Edition Cards

Bellsprout

Set: Jungle
Evolution: Into Weepinbell
Card Number: 49
Rarity: Common
English 1st Edition Price: $.50–$1
English 2nd Edition Price: $.25–$.50
Japanese Price: $.50–$1

This flower pokémon may look harmless and innocent, but look out—it's carnivorous! It has the power to grow stronger and likes to wrap up its prey before eating it. Its favorite thing to eat is bugs, so pokémon like Weedle should beware!

Butterfree

Set: Jungle
Evolution: From Metapod
Card Number: 33
Rarity: Uncommon
English 1st Edition Price: $2.50–$3.50
English 2nd Edition Price: $1.25–$2.25
Japanese Price: $2.25–$3.50

If only this pokémon listened to its own name and went on a "butter-free" diet! This pokémon might be a butterfly, but it's a giant one. It weighs more than 70 pounds! Unlike a regular butterfly, it can flap its wings quickly and create a tremendous windstorm.

Clefable

Set: Jungle
Evolution: From Clefairy
Card Number: 17/Holofoil #1
Rarity: Rare
English 1st Edition Holofoil Price: $15–$25
English 1st Edition Regular Price: $8–$15
English 2nd Edition Holofoil Price: $10–$18
English 2nd Edition Regular Price: $6–$10
Japanese Price: $12–$16

Clefables and clefaires, the pokémon clefables evolve from, guard the legendary Moon Stone, an element that can evolve pokémon. The evil Team Rocket once tried to steal the Moon Stone, but Ash and his friends saved the Moon Stone and its clefable guardians. Clefables can also copy any pokémon attack and use it against their opponents.

Cubone

Set: Jungle
Evolution: Into Marowak
Card Number: 50
Rarity: Common
English 1st Edition Price: $.50–$1
English 2nd Edition Price: $.25–$.50
Japanese Price: $.50–$1

The loneliest pokémon forms armor and weapons from the bones of other dead pokémon. Cubone wears a helmet made out of a skull and never takes it off, so no one ever sees its face. It's particularly good in combat against lightning pokémon, such as Pikachu.

Dodrio

Set: Jungle
Evolution: From Doduo
Card Number: 34
Rarity: Uncommon
English 1st Edition Price: $2.50–$3.50
English 2nd Edition Price: $1.25–$2.25
Japanese Price: $2.25–$3.50

In its evolved form, Dodrio gains an extra head—from two heads to three. Each of the ostrich-looking heads displays a different emotion—one happy, one sad, and one angry. Dodrio is toughest against fighting pokémon, such as Hitmonchan and Primeape.

Eevee

Set: Jungle
Evolution: Into Flareon, Jolteon, Vaporean
Card Number: 51
Rarity: Common
English 1st Edition Price: $.50–$1
English 2nd Edition Price: $.25–$.50
Japanese Price: $.50–$1

Eevee is one of the most unique pokémon in the game. Special elemental stones evolve it into three different pokémon—a fire stone for Flareon, a thunder stone for Jolteon, and a water stone for Vaporean. Like the fox it resembles, Eevee can attack quickly, especially with its tail.

Electrode

Set: Jungle
Evolution: From Voltorb
Card Number: 2/Holofoil #2
Rarity: Rare
English 1st Edition Holofoil Price: $12–$22
English 1st Edition Regular Price: $7–$14
English 2nd Edition Holofoil Price: $10–$15
English 2nd Edition Regular Price: $4–$8
Japanese Price: $10–$14

The Jungle version of this ball pokémon is one of the rarest you can find, if you're lucky. A misprint on the first edition Electrode has the same picture as the Basic set—a computer-animated Electrode looking straight at you, surrounded by a white aura. The correct picture for the first edition Jungle Electrode is a cartoon version of it grimacing and looking up to the left.

Exeggcute

Set: Jungle
Evolution: Into Exeggutor
Card Number: 52
Rarity: Common
English 1st Edition Price: $.50–$1
English 2nd Edition Price: $.25–$.50
Japanese Price: $.50–$1

Among the weirdest pokémon, these "egg-citable" purple egg pokémon quickly swarm around anything that gets close enough to "egg-samine" their nest. They're one of the few pokémon that use two energies: grass and psychic. Exeggcutes can evolve into their larger form with a leaf stone.

Exeggutor

Set: Jungle
Evolution: From Exeggcute
Card Number: 35
Rarity: Uncommon
English 1st Edition Price: $2.50–$3.50
English 2nd Edition Price: $1.25–$2.25
Japanese Price: $2.25–$3.50

One of the biggest pokémon, Exeggcutor is probably taller than you, standing at 6'7". It's so tall, it looks like a five-headed tree. It drops coconuts on its opponents for its attack. In its nine cartoon appearances, Exeggutor has never won a fight against another pokémon.

Fearow

Set: Jungle
Evolution: From Spearow
Card Number: 36
Rarity: Uncommon
English 1st Edition Price: $2.50–$3.50
English 2nd Edition Price: $1.25–$2.25
Japanese Price: $2.25–$3.50

This evolution of Spearow is much more fearsome, so you can see where it got its name. Complete with a beak and a red crown on the top of its head, Fearow looks like a giant rooster and is the size of the average third grader. Unlike a rooster, it can fly quickly for long periods of time.

Flareon

Set: Jungle
Evolution: From Eevee
Card Number: 19/Holofoil #3
Rarity: Rare
English 1st Edition Holofoil Price: $16–$28
English 1st Edition Regular Price: $8–$15
English 2nd Edition Holofoil Price: $12–$20
English 2nd Edition Regular Price: $6–$10
Japanese Price: $12–$16

This flame pokémon is one of the "hottest" cards in the Jungle set. Of course, the holofoil version is the more valuable of the two. It's one of the three poké-mon who evolve from Eevee, and, with a big fluffy body made of fire, it can launch a blazing attack that will burn almost any other pokémon.

Gloom

Set: Jungle
Evolution: From Oddish
Card Number: 37
Rarity: Uncommon
English 1st Edition Price: $2.50–$3.50
English 2nd Edition Price: $1.25–$2.25
Japanese Price: $2.25–$3.50

The middle evolution of the Oddish/Gloom/Vileplume trio, this weed pokémon is very slow, rarely moving from its grass habitat. Don't get too close, though—it can release spores that first stun you, then poison you. In Japanese, its name means "stinky flower."

Goldeen

Set: Jungle
Evolution: Into Seaking
Card Number: 53
Rarity: Common
English 1st Edition Price: $.50–$1
English 2nd Edition Price: $.25–$.50
Japanese Price: $.50–$1

If you have a lot of fish at home, you can see why this goldfish pokémon is very common. It's one of the weaker specimens, and it really doesn't have much going for it other than it evolves into the slightly more powerful Seaking. Don't expect much for this guy in a trade.

Jigglypuff

Set: Jungle
Evolution: Into Wigglytuff
Card Number: 54
Rarity: Common
English 1st Edition Price: $.60–$1.25
English 2nd Edition Price: $.25–$.50
Japanese Price: $.50–$1

It may look like a cute cross between a rabbit and a balloon and have the funniest sounding poké-mon name, but Jigglypuff can be formida-ble. Its sweet voice can sing a melody that puts other pokémon to sleep. In fact, it once put an entire city to sleep with its lullaby song.

Jolteon

Set: Jungle
Evolution: From Eevee
Card Number: 20/Holofoil #4
Rarity: Rare
English 1st Edition Holofoil Price: $16–$22
English 1st Edition Regular Price: $8–$15
English 2nd Edition Holofoil Price: $10–$18
English 2nd Edition Regular Price: $6–$10
Japanese Price: $12–$16

Like its cousin Pikachu, Jolteon is a lightning pokémon and is always generating electricity that can harm its opponents and even innocent bystanders. Besides being the second pokémon to evolve from Eevee, Jolteon is one of the three most valuable Jungle cards.

Kangaskhan

Set: Jungle
Evolution: None
Card Number: 21/Holofoil #5
Rarity: Rare
English 1st Edition Holofoil Price: $15–$25
English 1st Edition Regular Price: $8–$15
English 2nd Edition Holofoil Price: $10–$18
English 2nd Edition Regular Price: $6–$10
Japanese Price: $14–$18

One of the most powerful pokémon in the Jungle set, Kangaskhan has a kangaroo-shaped body built for battle. It carries its young in a pouch just like a kangaroo, and a baby kangaskhan will also fight if it has to.

Lickitung

Set: Jungle
Evolution: None
Card Number: 38
Rarity: Uncommon
English 1st Edition Price: $2.50–$3.50
English 2nd Edition Price: $1.25–$2.25
Japanese Price: $2.25–$3.50

Like a frog, Lickitung can shoot out its long tongue to catch food. The tongue also serves double duty, licking opponents in battle and paralyzing them. Lucky for those opponents, Lickitung doesn't evolve into anything nastier. In Japanese, its name means "tongue licker."

Mankey

Set: Jungle
Evolution: Into Primeape
Card Number: 55
Rarity: Common
English 1st Edition Price: $.50–$1
English 2nd Edition Price: $.25–$.50
Japanese Price: $.50–$1

This monkeylike pokémon has a pig's nose and humanlike arms that allow it to dance around quickly and avoid enemy attacks. It's a common card and not really valuable; however, it is one of the few basic pokémon that has a special pokémon power.

Marowak

Set: Jungle
Evolution: From Cubone
Card Number: 39
Rarity: Uncommon
English 1st Edition Price: $2.50–$3.50
English 2nd Edition Price: $1.25–$2.25
Japanese Price: $2.25–$3.50

Better than Cubone, which it evolves from, the brown and white, furry Marowak likes to fight other pokémon by throwing a bone as a weapon or using its spiky tail. Like boomerangs, the bones Marowak throws fly back to it if they miss their target.

Meowth

Set: Jungle
Evolution: Into Persian
Card Number: 56
Rarity: Common
English 1st Edition Price: $.50–$1
English 2nd Edition Price: $.25–$.50
Japanese Price: $.50–$1

One of the three Team Rocket members, Meowth is always trying to cause grief for Ash and Pikachu. Most of the pokémon can only repeat different syllables of their name, but Meowth can actually talk in whole sentences. It's one of the least-liked pokémon because of all the bad deeds it does.

Mr. Mime

Set: Jungle
Evolution: None
Card Number: 22/ Holofoil #6
Rarity: Rare
English 1st Edition Holofoil Price: $16–$25
English 1st Edition Regular Price: $8–$15
English 2nd Edition Holofoil Price: $12–$18
English 2nd Edition Regular Price: $6–$10
Japanese Price: $12–$16

Mr. Mime won't talk but will communicate by performing various physical charades to describe something. In the pokémon game, Mr. Mime is one of the best defenders and can really shut down big, powerful pokémon. This marionette-looking oddball is a favorite of collectors.

Nidoqueen

Set: Jungle
Evolution: From Nidorina
Card Number: 23/ Holofoil #7
Rarity: Rare
English 1st Edition Holofoil Price: $14–$22
English 1st Edition Regular Price: $8–$15
English 2nd Edition Holofoil Price: $12–$18
English 2nd Edition Regular Price: $6–$9
Japanese Price: $10–$15

In the Basic set, the male Nidoran trio evolves up to Nidoking. In the Jungle set, the female Nidoran trio evolves up to Nidoqueen. If you manage to get her Nidoking boyfriend into play, her attacks and dinosaurlike body are more powerful.

Nidoran (female)

Set: Jungle
Evolution: Into Nidorina
Card Number: 57
Rarity: Common
English 1st Edition Price: $.50–$1
English 2nd Edition Price: $.25–$.50
Japanese Price: $.50–$1

Pokémon are neither male nor female, except for the Nidoran clan—the boys are in the Basic set, the girls in Jungle. Jungle's Nidoran is one of the strongest basic pokémon, both in how much damage she can take and how much she can dish out! Unfortunately for collectors, this fact doesn't translate into value, since she's an easy-to-get common.

Nidorina

Set: Jungle
Evolution: From Nidoran/Into Nidoqueen
Card Number: 40
Rarity: Uncommon
English 1st Edition Price: $2.50–$3.50
English 2nd Edition Price: $1.25–$2.25
Japanese Price: $2.25–$3.50

The middle evolver, Nidorina likes to attack with claws and fangs. The Nidoran clan grows a lot when evolving. Nidorina is three times bigger than Nidoran, and Nidoqueen is three times bigger than Nidorina! She has spots like Nidoran but loses them when she gains armor as Nidoqueen.

Oddish

Set: Jungle
Evolution: Into Gloom
Card Number: 58
Rarity: Common
English 1st Edition Price: $.50–$1
English 2nd Edition Price: $.25–$.50
Japanese Price: $.50–$1

Like its name suggests, this weed pokémon may be the oddest-looking creature in the bunch. Sort of like a blue onion with spiky stalk hair and marshmallow feet, Oddish is a nocturnal animal, hiding during the day and wandering around and spreading its seeds at night.

Paras

Set: Jungle
Evolution: Into Parasect
Card Number: 59
Rarity: Common
English 1st Edition Price: $.50–$1
English 2nd Edition Price: $.25–$.50
Japanese Price: $.50–$1

What happens when a mushroom meets a crab? You get Paras and its evolution, Parasect. Paras is one of the weakest pokémon going, so don't expect much out of it in battle. It's very tiny and doesn't travel very far, so, no, it has never been to the French city of Paris.

Parasect

Set: Jungle
Evolution: From Paras
Card Number: 41
Rarity: Uncommon
English 1st Edition Price: $2.50–$3.50
English 2nd Edition Price: $1.25–$2.25
Japanese Price: $2.25–$3.50

If you thought Paras was bad, you'll be disappointed in its evolution, Parasect. In fact, the two of them may be the least powerful evolution team in the world of pokémon. And since neither has a holofoil version, they'll most likely end up at the bottom of your trading pile.

Persian

Set: Jungle
Evolution: From Meowth
Card Number: 42
Rarity: Uncommon
English 1st Edition Price: $2.25–$3.25
English 2nd Edition Price: $1–$2
Japanese Price: $2.25–$3.50

Named after a cat's purr rather than the ancient Persian civilization, this classy cat pokémon is the evolution of the mischievous Meowth. Unfortunately, Meowth is actually more powerful than the evolved Persian, which makes it a less valuable card than other uncommons.

Pidgeot

Set: Jungle
Evolution: From Pidgeotto
Card Number: 24/Holofoil #8
Rarity: Rare
English 1st Edition Holofoil Price: $15–$22
English 1st Edition Regular Price: $8–$15
English 2nd Edition Holofoil Price: $10–$16
English 2nd Edition Regular Price: $6–$10
Japanese Price: $12–$15

Looking like a large falcon rather than the bird that is closer to its name, the pigeon, Pidgeot will easily beat up any fighting pokémon. With a flap of its wings, it can remove big pokémon, such as Blastoise and Charizard, from battle with little risk to itself. Its holofoil version is a sought-after card by all serious trainers.

Pikachu

Set: Jungle
Evolution: Into Raichu
Card Number: 60
Rarity: Common
English 1st Edition Price: $.60–$1.25
English 2nd Edition Price: $.25–$.50
Japanese Price: $1–$2

By far, Pikachu is the most dominating pokémon in the cartoon series. Ash's little pal has won 21 battles against other pokémon and lost only 6. The Jungle version of the little yellow mouse is much more powerful than the Basic card. Even though it's a common, it's Pikachu and so receives a two in collectibility instead of a one.

Pinsir

Set: Jungle
Evolution: None
Card Number: 25/Holofoil #9

Rarity: Rare
English 1st Edition Holofoil Price: \$15–\$22
English 1st Edition Regular Price: \$8–\$14
English 2nd Edition Holofoil Price: \$10–\$16
English 2nd Edition Regular Price: \$6–\$10
Japanese Price: \$12–\$15

If you're not careful, this aggressive bug pokémon will charge out of the jungle and pinch you between its two sharp horns. It's one of the strongest grass pokémon, and though it doesn't evolve into anything, it can fight very well all by itself. For fans who like big, strong pokémon, this is a must-have card.

Primeape

Set: Jungle
Evolution: From Mankey
Card Number: 43
Rarity: Uncommon
English 1st Edition Price: \$2.50–\$3.50
English 2nd Edition Price: \$1–\$2
Japanese Price: \$2.25–\$3.50

Speaking of big, strong pokémon, Mankey's evolver, Primeape, is another monstrously powerful pokémon. Charging around and attacking everything in sight, Primeape is always angry and will keep going and going until its enemies are crushed. In Japanese, its name means "mad monkey."

Rapidash

Set: Jungle
Evolution: From Ponyta
Card Number: 44
Rarity: Uncommon
English 1st Edition Price: \$2.50–\$3.50
English 2nd Edition Price: \$1–\$2
Japanese Price: \$2.25–\$3.50

This fiery horse pokémon is always racing other pokémon to prove it's the fastest creature in the land. In the cartoon, Ash once rode a rapidash against Team Rocket and had to avoid a series of "accidents" Team Rocket had set up to stop him. Rapidash was the fastest and won the race, embarrassing Team Rocket.

Rhydon

Set: Jungle
Evolution: From Rhyhorn
Card Number: 45
Rarity: Uncommon
English 1st Edition Price: \$2.50–\$3.50
English 2nd Edition Price: \$1–\$2
Japanese Price: \$2.25–\$3.50

Not many pokémon reach triple digits in hit points, but Rhydon has a whopping 100, which makes it one of the toughest pokémon around! How did it get to be so tough? It lives deep underground where temperatures can reach more than 2,000 degrees, and it has developed a rock-hard skin to protect itself.

Rhyhorn

Set: Jungle
Evolution: Into Rhydon
Card Number: 61
Rarity: Common
English 1st Edition Price: $.50–$1
English 2nd Edition Price: $.25–$.50
Japanese Price: $.50–$1

Though Rhyhorn can evolve into the even tougher Rhydon, Rhyhorn itself has nearly invulnerable armor, 1,000 times stronger than human bones! Very powerful for a common card, it's still not worth that much, unless you plan on trading to make a set with Rhydon.

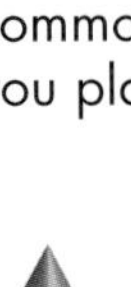

Scyther

Set: Jungle
Evolution: None
Card Number: 10/Holofoil #10
Rarity: Rare
English 1st Edition Holofoil Price: $16–$28
English 1st Edition Regular Price: $8–$18
English 2nd Edition Holofoil Price: $12–$18
English 2nd Edition Regular Price: $6–$10
Japanese Price: $12–$18

This bug-meets-dinosaur pokémon is among the fiercest fighters in the game. Sharp, slashing wings combine for a big attack, and it's highly resistant to fighting pokémon, such as Hitmonlee. For game players, Scyther is one of the best pokémon and is very valuable.

Seaking

Set: Jungle
Evolution: From Goldeen
Card Number: 46
Rarity: Uncommon
English 1st Edition Price: $2.50–$3.50
English 2nd Edition Price: $1.25–$2.25
Japanese Price: $2.25–$3.50

The brilliant colors of this underwater goldfish pokémon make it an easy target, so it likes to hide amidst the reds, greens, and yellows of the sea-floor coral. Like a unicorn, it has a single horn on its head that it can use to protect itself. Its status as king of the sea, like its name implies, is a bit doubtful.

Snorlax

Set: Jungle
Evolution: None
Card Number: 27/Holofoil #11
Rarity: Rare
English 1st Edition Holofoil Price: $15–$24
English 1st Edition Regular Price: $8–$14
English 2nd Edition Holofoil Price: $12–$18
English 2nd Edition Regular Price: $6–$10
Japanese Price: $10–$16

Snorlax is the largest pokémon, weighing more than 1,000 pounds! Unfortunately, its large size makes it extremely lazy and sleepy. It spends more time asleep than awake, but when it shakes the sleepy dust out, it can be a difficult opponent. It's so cute, and the holofoil version is highly collectible.

Spearow

Set: Jungle
Evolution: Into Fearow
Card Number: 62
Rarity: Common
English 1st Edition Price: $.50–$1
English 2nd Edition Price: $.25–$.50
Japanese Price: $.50–$1

In Japanese, its name means "demon sparrow." Living up to its name, this tiny bird pokémon can fight with its beak or duplicate the attack that its opponent used on it, no matter how powerful! Like its evolution, Fearow, it can easily overcome fighting pokémon, like Marowak.

Tauros

Set: Jungle
Evolution: None
Card Number: 47
Rarity: Uncommon
English 1st Edition Price: $2.50–$3.50
English 2nd Edition Price: $1.25–$2.25
Japanese Price: $2.25–$3.50

Since it is only found in remote locations, the bull-like Tauros is one of the more difficult pokémon to catch. Just like real-life bulls, you don't want to threaten Tauros by getting too close or it will charge and try to spear you with its long horns.

Vaporean

Set: Jungle
Evolution: From Eevee
Card Number: 28/ Holofoil #12
Rarity: Rare
English 1st Edition Holofoil Price: $15–$24
English 1st Edition Regular Price: $8–$14
English 2nd Edition Holofoil Price: $10–$15
English 2nd Edition Regular Price: $6–$8
Japanese Price: $10–$14

The third evolution of Eevee looks like a mermaid. Though many other pokémon may be more familiar to you, such as Electabuzz, Ditto, Diglett, and Clefairy, Vaporean actually had more appearances during the first season of the cartoon than they did. And though Vaporeon may be a holofoil, its game power is only so-so, which drops the card's collectibility slightly.

Venomoth

Set: Jungle
Evolution: From Venonat
Card Number: 29/ Holofoil #13
Rarity: Rare
English 1st Edition Holofoil Price: $14–$22
English 1st Edition Regular Price: $8–$14
English 2nd Edition Holofoil Price: $10–$15
English 2nd Edition Regular Price: $6–$9
Japanese Price: $10–$16

This 28-pound moth uses a variety of poisons to incapacitate its foes. Venomoth has the ability to change to any colored energy type. The holofoil version makes Venomoth collectible, despite its average power level.

Venonat

Set: Jungle
Evolution: Into Venomoth
Card Number: 63
Rarity: Common
English 1st Edition Price: $.50–$1
English 2nd Edition Price: $.25–$.50
Japanese Price: $.50–$1

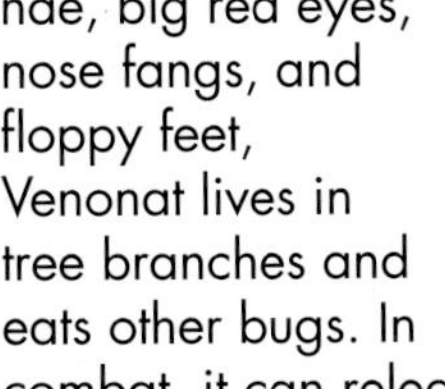

A furball with antennae, big red eyes, nose fangs, and floppy feet, Venonat lives in tree branches and eats other bugs. In combat, it can release a spore from its body that will stun opposing pokémon. It doesn't like fighting fire pokémon.

Victreebel

Set: Jungle
Evolution: From Weepinbell
Card Number: 30/Holofoil #14
Rarity: Rare
English 1st Edition Holofoil Price: $14–$22
English 1st Edition Regular Price: $8–$14
English 2nd Edition Holofoil Price: $10–$15
English 2nd Edition Regular Price: $6–$9
Japanese Price: $10–$16

Victreebel cleverly lures other pokémon to it, then wraps its leaves around the victim and oozes acid to weaken its prey. The highest evolution of the Bellsprout trio is the most valuable of the bunch and the only one really worth anything.

Vileplume

Set: Jungle
Evolution: From Gloom
Card Number: 31/Holofoil #15
Rarity: Rare
English 1st Edition Holofoil Price: $14–$22
English 1st Edition Regular Price: $8–$14
English 2nd Edition Holofoil Price: $10–$15
English 2nd Edition Regular Price: $6–$9
Japanese Price: $10–$16

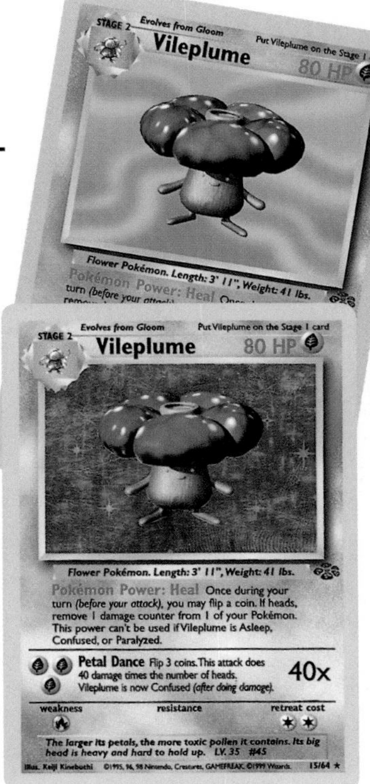

This flower pokémon wields a devastating attack. It can deal up to 120 hit points of damage in a single strike! Its name and appearance are warning signs—Vileplume looks like a poisonous mushroom. This valuable pokémon is one of the three best cards in Jungle for game players.

Weepinbell

Set: Jungle
Evolution: From Bellsprout/Into Victreebel
Card Number: 48
Rarity: Uncommon
English 1st Edition Price: $2.50–$3.50
English 2nd Edition Price: $1.25–$2.25
Japanese Price: $2.25–$3.50

Shaped like a bell, this flycatcher pokémon weighs as much as a large cat. Trainers specializing in grass pokémon use Weepinbell for its razor-sharp leaves, poison that weakens an opposing pokémon, and acid that can completely dissolve its foe.

Wigglytuff

Set: Jungle
Evolution: From Jigglypuff
Card Number: 32/Holofoil #16
Rarity: Rare
English 1st Edition Holofoil Price: $16–$25
English 1st Edition Regular Price: $8–$16
English 2nd Edition Holofoil Price: $12–$18
English 2nd Edition Regular Price: $6–$10
Japanese Price: $12–$18

Wigglytuff is a very valuable pokémon due to its cuteness factor and special powers. Like the smaller Jigglypuff, it can also lull pokémon to sleep with its song and inflate to an enormous size when agitated.

Trainer Card

Poké Ball

Set: Jungle
Card Number: 64
Rarity: Common
English 1st Edition Price: $.50–$1
English 2nd Edition Price: $.25–$.50
Japanese Price: $.50–$1

The red-and-white balls with the little button on top are found on the back of every poké-mon card. Pokémon trainers hunt out in the wild with these balls, throwing them at weakened poké-mon and capturing them. Poké ball is the only trainer in Jungle.

Fossil Expansion

48 Cards in Japanese Edition; 62 Cards in English First and Second Editions

Aerodactyl

Set: Fossil
Evolution: From Mysterious Fossil
Card Number: 16/ Holofoil #1
Rarity: Rare
English 1st Edition Holo-foil Price: $14–$20
English 1st Edition Regu-lar Price: $5–$10
English 2nd Edition Holofoil Price: $6–$12
English 2nd Edition Regular Price: $4–$8
Japanese Price: $20–$30

The game's oldest pokémon hails from prehistoric times. Its name comes from a merging of the words "aero" for flying and "dactyl," as in pterodactyl. Aerodactyl is one of the most powerful pokémon, because no pokémon can evolve once it's in play. This makes it one of the most valuable Fossil cards.

Arbok

Set: Fossil
Evolution: From Ekans
Card Number: 31
Rarity: Uncommon
English 1st Edition Price: $2.50–$3.50
English 2nd Edition Price: $1.25–$2.25
Japanese Price: $2.25–$3.50

Arbok looks like a giant, purple cobra. And, like a snake, it can strike quickly and inject poison into its victims using its fangs. Whether the clownlike marking on its underside is meant to scare its enemies or amuse them, we're still not sure. But we do know that other arboks use them to tell each other apart.

Articuno

Set: Fossil
Evolution: None
Card Number: 17/Holofoil #2
Rarity: Rare
English 1st Edition Holofoil Price: $10–$16
English 1st Edition Regular Price: $5–$8
English 2nd Edition Holofoil Price: $6–$12
English 2nd Edition Regular Price: $4–$6
Japanese Price: $16–$22

This legendary birdlike pokémon might be one of the most difficult to spot, since it's very rare and lives in super-cold temperatures. It's powerful enough to bring a blizzard against its foes, but you'll want to stay clear. It has a good chance of hitting friendly pokémon with this attack as well.

Cloyster

Set: Fossil
Evolution: From Shellder
Card Number: 32
Rarity: Uncommon
English 1st Edition Price: $2.50–$3.50
English 2nd Edition Price: $1.25–$2.25
Japanese Price: $2.25–$3.50

Talk about protective—this shell-like pokémon has never let anyone see its insides. It's equipped with a spike cannon that can fire up to five times against an opponent in rapid succession. Because it's a water-based pokémon, it doesn't like electricity and spends little time on land.

Ditto

Set: Fossil
Evolution: None
Card Number: 18/Holofoil #3
Rarity: Rare
English 1st Edition Holofoil Price: $12–$18
English 1st Edition Regular Price: $6–$10
English 2nd Edition Holofoil Price: $8–$14
English 2nd Edition Regular Price: $4–$8
Japanese Price: $12–$16

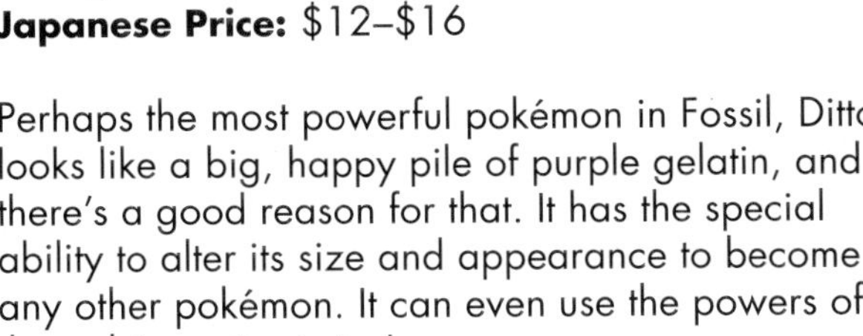

Perhaps the most powerful pokémon in Fossil, Ditto looks like a big, happy pile of purple gelatin, and there's a good reason for that. It has the special ability to alter its size and appearance to become any other pokémon. It can even use the powers of the pokémon it mimics!

Dragonite

Set: Fossil
Evolution: From Dragonair
Card Number: 19/Holofoil #4
Rarity: Rare
English 1st Edition Holofoil Price: $12–$18
English 1st Edition Regular Price: $5–$10
English 2nd Edition Holofoil Price: $6–$12
English 2nd Edition Regular Price: $4–$8
Japanese Price: $20–$30

One of the biggest pokémon with 100 hit points, its name pretty much tells you what it is—a pokémon that is mostly dragon. Unlike Dragonite from the Basic set, this Dragonite is much faster, able to quickly swoop up and take the place of one of your other pokémon in battle.

Ekans

Set: Fossil
Evolution: Into Arbok
Card Number: 46
Rarity: Common
English 1st Edition Price: $.50–$1
English 2nd Edition Price: $.25–$.50
Japanese Price: $.50–$1

This snake pokémon evolves into the cobralike Arbok and weighs more than an average snake. Unlike a real snake whose colors help it blend in with its surroundings, Ekans's skin is a brilliant purple with yellow rings. It's a solid pokémon in the game, because it can both poison and paralyze. Ekans is snake spelled backward.

Gastly

Set: Fossil
Evolution: Into Haunter
Card Number: 33
Rarity: Uncommon
English 1st Edition Price: $2.50–$3.50
English 2nd Edition Price: $1.25–$2.25
Japanese Price: $2.25–$3.50

No one knows where this gas pokémon comes from, but we do know where it's going—it's eventually evolving into Haunter and then Gengar. In the game, it has very good powers, including the ability to retrieve energy cards from your discard pile and return them to your hand.

Gengar

Set: Fossil
Evolution: From Haunter
Card Number: 20/Holofoil #5
Rarity: Rare
English 1st Edition Holofoil Price: $8–$14
English 1st Edition Regular Price: $5–$8
English 2nd Edition Holofoil Price: $6–$10
English 2nd Edition Regular Price: $4–$6
Japanese Price: $12–$16

Gengar is the only ghostly pokémon who has a fully formed body. It's one of the meanest pokémon: It likes to laugh in people's faces when they get scared, and it will curse pokémon that annoy it. Gengar is the top evolution of the Gastly trio, and its card is valuable because it's so powerful.

Geodude

Set: Fossil
Evolution: Into Graveler
Card Number: 47
Rarity: Common
English 1st Edition Price: $.50–$1
English 2nd Edition Price: $.25–$.50
Japanese Price: $.50–$1

It's hip to be this "dude." Disguised as a rock, Geodude can surprise other pokémon and barrage them with stones. These stones can do an unlimited amount of damage, depending on how lucky Geodude gets with its hits. It doesn't like fighting grass pokémon, such as Venusaur.

Golbat

Set: Fossil
Evolution: From Zubat
Card Number: 34
Rarity: Uncommon
English 1st Edition Price: $2.50–$3.50
English 2nd Edition Price: $1.25–$2.25
Japanese Price: $2.25–$3.50

Like a vampire that can suck your blood, Golbat can drain your energy. If you think that's scary, you haven't seen Golbat in person. It's more than 120 pounds and gets even larger when it drains energy from its victims. Fighting pokémon, such as Hitmonchan and Geodude, have a hard time beating the flying Golbat.

Golduck

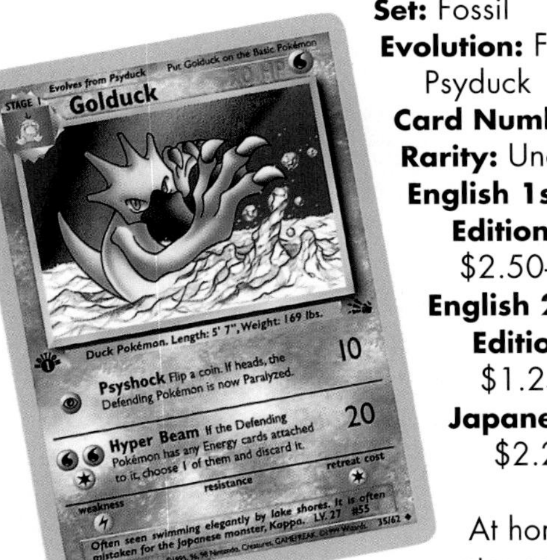

Set: Fossil
Evolution: From Psyduck
Card Number: 35
Rarity: Uncommon
English 1st Edition Price: $2.50–$3.50
English 2nd Edition Price: $1.25–$2.25
Japanese Price: $2.25–$3.50

At home in the water and on shore, Golduck swims elegantly and fights fiercely on land with its thick claws. It's one of the very few pokémon who can use more than one energy type: Its mental attack uses psychic energy, and its beam attack uses water energy.

Golem

Set: Fossil
Evolution: From Graveler
Card Number: 36
Rarity: Uncommon
English 1st Edition Price: $2.50–$3.50
English 2nd Edition Price: $1.25–$2.25
Japanese Price: $2.25–$3.50

If you were to explode a bomb next to Golem, its rock-hard skin would shield it from most of the damage. So you can see why it's a very powerful poké-mon. But the crazy thing is that Golem blows itself up when it attacks. This takes out every enemy in the area, but this doesn't do much for its own com-plexion.

Graveler

Set: Fossil
Evolution: From Geodude/Into Golem
Card Number: 37
Rarity: Uncommon
English 1st Edition Price: $2.50–$3.50
English 2nd Edition Price: $1.25–$2.25
Japanese Price: $2.25–$3.50

Graveler doesn't walk; it rolls around to move. As the middle evolution of Geodude and Golem, it has both strong defensive and offensive powers, which make it a tough monster to take on. In its cartoon fights against other pokémon, Graveler has never lost.

Grimer

Set: Fossil
Evolution: Into Muk
Card Number: 48
Rarity: Common
English 1st Edition Price: $.50–$1
English 2nd Edition Price: $.25–$.50
Japanese Price: $.50–$1

Remember the monster from *The Blob*? Grimer takes after that famous movie monster, appearing as a gooey, purple mess of sludge that feeds on pollution. It's tough to deal damage to this pokémon, because it just splits apart. But Grimer has little trouble dealing damage with its body's nasty chemicals. In Japanese, its name means "stickiness."

Haunter

Set: Fossil
Evolution: From Gastly/Into Gengar
Card Number: 21/Holofoil #6
Rarity: Rare
English 1st Edition Holofoil Price: $8–$12
English 1st Edition Regular Price: $6–$8
English 2nd Edition Holofoil Price: $6–$10
English 2nd Edition Regular Price: $4–$6
Japanese Price: $9–$15

Is this pokémon a ghost or a creature from another dimension? No one knows for sure, but it can move easily through solid objects and frequently avoids pokémon attacks, many of which pass harmlessly through its body. Like its name implies, Haunter can enter your dreams and cause nightmares.

Hitmonlee

Set: Fossil
Evolution: None
Card Number: 22/Holofoil #7
Rarity: Rare
English 1st Edition Holofoil Price: $14–$20
English 1st Edition Regular Price: $6–$12

English 2nd Edition Holofoil Price: $8–$16
English 2nd Edition Regular Price: $5–$10
Japanese Price: $12–$20

Hitmonlee is named after martial arts actor Bruce Lee. It is showing off its moves with a flexible high kick! Its legs can actually extend long distances. In fact, it could battle one pokémon and kick another one not even in the fight! Since it's such a tough fighter and fits well in a "Haymaker" deck, Hitmonlee is one of the most valuable cards in this set.

Horsea

Set: Fossil
Evolution: Into Seadra
Card Number: 49
Rarity: Common
English 1st Edition Price: $.50–$1
English 2nd Edition Price: $.25–$.50
Japanese Price: $.50–$1

Believe it or not, this little fish is actually a dragon pokémon. It's a weak pokémon, but it has developed some self-defense skills. Like a squid, it can expel an inky substance out of its mouth, confusing or blinding its attacker so that Horsea can make a stealthy escape.

Hypno

Set: Fossil
Evolution: From Drowzee
Card Number: 23/Holofoil #8

Rarity: Rare
English 1st Edition Holofoil Price: \$8–\$12
English 1st Edition Regular Price: \$6–\$8
English 2nd Edition Holofoil Price: \$7–\$10
English 2nd Edition Regular Price: \$4–\$6
Japanese Price: \$10–\$14

Hypno carries a ring on a chain that it swings back and forth to—what else—hypnotize its opponent. This psychic pokémon has the gift of foretelling the future and will blast enemies with a mental attack when angered. Even with a fully developed mind, it's vulnerable to psychic attacks.

Kabuto

Set: Fossil
Evolution: From Mysterious Fossil/Into Kabutops
Card Number: 50
Rarity: Common
English 1st Edition Price: \$.50–\$1
English 2nd Edition Price: \$.25–\$.50
Japanese Price: \$.50–\$1

Regular pokémon evolve from other pokémon. Not Kabuto. It evolves from a mysterious fossil found on the ocean floor into a shellfish pokémon. Kabuto has a special defense that takes only half damage from any attack against it. For further defense, it hides in its shell.

Kabutops

Set: Fossil
Evolution: From Kabuto
Card Number: 24/Holofoil #9
Rarity: Rare
English 1st Edition Holofoil Price: \$8–\$14
English 1st Edition Regular Price: \$6–\$10
English 2nd Edition Holofoil Price: \$6–\$12
English 2nd Edition Regular Price: \$4–\$6
Japanese Price: \$12–\$16

Its sleek body moves deftly in the water, and it's very dangerous on land with its bladelike claws. Though a shellfish pokémon, it looks more like an armored praying mantis. That same armor can absorb physical blows and shake off pokémon poisons, acids, and teeth.

Kingler

Set: Fossil
Evolution: From Krabby
Card Number: 38
Rarity: Uncommon
English 1st Edition Price: \$2.50–\$3.50
English 2nd Edition Price: \$1.25–\$2.25
Japanese Price: \$2.25–\$3.50

Kingler is slow and can easily be harmed, but that just causes it to get angry and deal even more damage to the opposing pokémon! This crablike creature is dubbed a pincer pokémon because of its giant lobster claw and the fact that it might squeeze your cheek harder than your Aunt Zelda does.

Krabby

Set: Fossil
Evolution: Into Kingler
Card Number: 51
Rarity: Common
English 1st Edition Price: $.50–$1
English 2nd Edition Price: $.25–$.50
Japanese Price: $.50–$1

Crabs usually hang out in groups; the same goes for Krabby and its friends. In the game, Krabby can easily fetch other krabbies whenever it wants. They all have vise-like grips and a tough shell defense, so other pokémon won't want to attack unless they're fully prepared.

Magmar

Set: Fossil
Evolution: None
Card Number: 39
Rarity: Uncommon
English 1st Edition Price: $2.50–$3.50
English 2nd Edition Price: $1.25–$2.25
Japanese Price: $2.25–$3.50

Magma means molten hot lava, so you can guess where this poké-mon likes to spend its time. Strangely enough, this fire pokémon has a poison attack, which it normally reserves for grass pokémon. Beginning trainers don't even try to catch magmars, because they are so difficult to locate.

Lapras

Set: Fossil
Evolution: None
Card Number: 25/Holofoil #10
Rarity: Rare
English 1st Edition Holofoil Price: $8–$14
English 1st Edition Regular Price: $6–$10
English 2nd Edition Holofoil Price: $6–$12
English 2nd Edition Regular Price: $4–$6
Japanese Price: $12–$16

The toughest basic pokémon in Fossil, Lapras can blast water at its opponents and confuse them—but neither attack is very strong. Thoughtless hunters have killed so many of its kind that they are now an endangered species, so collectors might want to snatch up these "Loch Ness Monster"–like pokémon before they all disappear.

Magneton

Set: Fossil
Evolution: From Magnemite
Card Number: 26/Holofoil #11
Rarity: Rare
English 1st Edition Holofoil Price: $8–$12
English 1st Edition Regular Price: $6–$8
English 2nd Edition Holofoil Price: $6–$10
English 2nd Edition Regular Price: $4–$6
Japanese Price: $12–$16

With enough doodads to put Inspector Gadget to shame, Magneton is actually several smaller mag-nemites linked together. So many magnetic fields surround this pokémon that it's highly unstable and can explode at any time! If it manages to stick around, it's a potent pokémon that can deal serious damage.

Mew

Set: Fossil
Evolution: None
Card Number: Not known
Rarity: Rare/Holofoil
English 1st Edition Holofoil Price: Mew was removed from the English editions and will be available only to members of the Pokémon Players League.
Japanese Price: $36–$46

The adorable, playful Mew was the hero of the first pokémon movie. The rarest pokémon of all, it's very shy and doesn't like to fight other pokémon. If it is forced to attack, it creates pink energy balloons that act like giant, bouncy bubble gum bubbles. Mew is a super-valuable card because it's only available through the Wizards of the Coast Pokémon Player's League.

Moltres

Set: Fossil
Evolution: None
Card Number: 27/Holofoil #12
Rarity: Rare
English 1st Edition Holofoil Price: $10–$16
English 1st Edition Regular Price: $7–$10
English 2nd Edition Holofoil Price: $8–$12
English 2nd Edition Regular Price: $6–$8
Japanese Price: $14–$18

Hot and spicy are the words that come to mind for this pokémon's flaming wings! Charizard may have more punch than this legendary pokémon, but Moltres can swoop down on its prey and blaze it to cinders. Even though its game ability isn't that good, Moltres is still collectible if you snag the holofoil version.

Muk

Set: Fossil
Evolution: From Grimer
Card Number: 28/Holofoil #13
Rarity: Rare
English 1st Edition Holofoil Price: $8–$14
English 1st Edition Regular Price: $6–$10
English 2nd Edition Holofoil Price: $6–$12
English 2nd Edition Regular Price: $5–$8
Japanese Price: $12–$16

Muk's toxic fumes are so potent they shut down all pokémon powers in the area. Like Grimer, who it evolves from, Muk is a sludge-based pokémon, and every inch of its oozing form is poisonous. Smart pokémon won't battle it. Only psychic pokémon challenge it, and then only at a distance.

Omanyte

Set: Fossil
Evolution: From Mysterious Fossil
Card Number: 52
Rarity: Common
English 1st Edition Price: $.50–$1
English 2nd Edition Price: $.25–$.50
Japanese Price: $.50–$1

It may be a basic pokémon, but, when in play, Omanyte has the nifty ability to make your opponent play with all his or her cards face up. Though it's extinct, scientists have brought several omanytes back to life from fossil specimens using genetic engineering.

Omastar

Set: Fossil
Evolution: From Omanyte
Card Number: 40
Rarity: Uncommon
English 1st Edition Price: $2.50–$3.50
English 2nd Edition Price: $1.25–$2.25
Japanese Price: $2.25–$3.50

This pokémon might have been formidable in prehistoric times, but it has only recently been discovered after a mysterious fossil surfaced. It can attack with a jet of water and, if it can manage to get in close, will bite you with its squidlike beak.

Psyduck

Set: Fossil
Evolution: Into Golduck
Card Number: 53
Rarity: Common
English 1st Edition Price: $.50–$1
English 2nd Edition Price: $.25–$.50
Japanese Price: $.50–$1

Another pokémon with both psychic and water abilities, Psyduck can "fowl" up your opponent's strategy, since its psychic power prevents trainer cards from being played by your opponent. Ironically, its evolution, Golduck, isn't golden in color, whereas Psyduck is. Weird.

Raichu

Set: Fossil
Evolution: From Pikachu
Card Number: 29/Holofoil #14
Rarity: Rare
English 1st Edition Holofoil Price: $8–$16
English 1st Edition Regular Price: $7–$12
English 2nd Edition Holofoil Price: $8–$14
English 2nd Edition Regular Price: $5–$8
Japanese Price: $16–$22

Pikachu's bigger self has collectors drooling. First, there's the cuteness factor—there's something about pudgy, yellow, electric mice that fans can't resist. Second, Raichu's formidable hit points and shock attack make him a big gun in the game. Third, Raichu is shiny, and we all know that holofoils are almost as valuable as Richie Rich's credit card.

Sandslash

Set: Fossil
Evolution: From Sandshrew
Card Number: 41
Rarity: Uncommon
English 1st Edition Price: $2.50–$3.50
English 2nd Edition Price: $1.25–$2.25
Japanese Price: $2.25–$3.50

It took a while for Sandshrew to evolve, but here Sandslash is in Fossil. Where Sandshrew concentrated on defense, Sandslash, as its name implies, wields two furious attacks. Its swipes can do a ton of damage in the game for a very cheap cost, and its 70 hit points are nothing to sneeze at.

Seadra

Set: Fossil
Evolution: From Horsea
Card Number: 42
Rarity: Uncommon
English 1st Edition Price: $2.50–$3.50
English 2nd Edition Price: $1.25–$2.25
Japanese Price: $2.25–$3.50

Sea horses are charming in your fish tank, but what happens when you meet a 3-foot, 55-pound one in the wild? First you swim away, then you marvel at its incredible agility and accuracy with a water gun that can pound lesser pokémon into oblivion.

Shellder

Set: Fossil
Evolution: Into Cloyster
Card Number: 54
Rarity: Common
English 1st Edition Price: $.50–$1
English 2nd Edition Price: $.25–$.50
Japanese Price: $.50–$1

With only 30 hit points, Shellder seems very vulnerable, but it's not really. If it hides in its shell, it can't be harmed by any attack, whether it be a natural disaster or a menacing pokémon going nuclear on it. Should it decide to attack, it lets out a supersonic blast that can confuse other pokémon.

Slowbro

Set: Fossil
Evolution: From Slowpoke
Card Number: 43
Rarity: Uncommon
English 1st Edition Price: $2.50–$3.50
English 2nd Edition Price: $1.25–$2.25
Japanese Price: $2.25–$3.50

Slowbro looks a little odd—it's a pink bear with a living conch shell clamped onto its tail. How did it get that way? Slowbro loves to fish with its tail, and one day a hermit crab latched onto its tail and decided to stay. Slowbro could actually be related to Alakazam; it has a damage-absorbing ability very similar to Alakazam's.

Slowpoke

Set: Fossil
Evolution: Into Slowbro
Card Number: 55
Rarity: Common
English 1st Edition Price: $.50–$1
English 2nd Edition Price: $.25–$.50
Japanese Price: $.50–$1

This dopey pokémon's picture looks like an animation out of *The Simpsons* TV show, and, appropriately enough, you can't take it very seriously. It can't fight at all—it can only take a beating and retrieve a trainer card from the discard pile by expending psychic energy. We feel bad for Slowpoke; that's why he's in our collection.

Tentacool

Set: Fossil
Evolution: Into Tentacruel
Card Number: 56
Rarity: Common
English 1st Edition Price: $.50–$1
English 2nd Edition Price: $.25–$.50
Japanese Price: $.50–$1

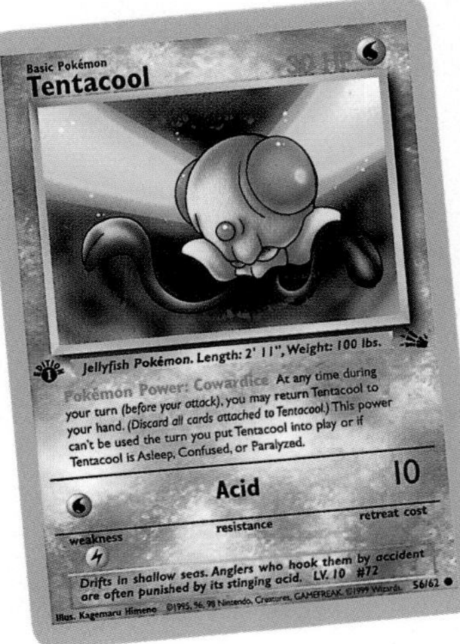

Tentacool is really timid: It doesn't like to fight other pokémon, but, if it does, it can defend itself with a special acid it releases into the water. In game terms, Tentacool has the neat ability to jump back into your hand from play any time during your turn to protect itself.

Tentacruel

Set: Fossil
Evolution: From Tentacool
Card Number: 44
Rarity: Uncommon
English 1st Edition Price: $2.50–$3.50
English 2nd Edition Price: $1.25–$2.25
Japanese Price: $2.25–$3.50

The crueler evolution of Tentacool has 12 different jellyfishlike tentacles that can sting enemy pokémon and poison them. Unlike most jellyfish, it's not transparent, so you can see this 120-pound monster coming. Trainers who want to capture a tentacruel would be wise to knock it out with a lightning pokémon.

Weezing

Set: Fossil
Evolution: From Koffing
Card Number: 45
Rarity: Uncommon
English 1st Edition Price: $2.50–$3.50
English 2nd Edition Price: $1.25–$2.25
Japanese Price: $2.25–$3.50

When two stars meet, they fuse together to make a bigger star. Same thing happens with two koffings: When their poison gases mix together, they gradually metamorph into a weezing. This poison gas pokémon can let loose a smog attack and can explode, suffocating other pokémon in the area.

Zapdos

Set: Fossil
Evolution: None
Card Number: 30/Holofoil #15
Rarity: Rare
English 1st Edition Holofoil Price: $8–$16
English 1st Edition Regular Price: $6–$10
English 2nd Edition Holofoil Price: $8–$14
English 2nd Edition Regular Price: $5–$8
Japanese Price: $15–$20

It may look like Big Bird getting shocked, but it's not—it's Zapdos, the largest electric pokémon in the game. The Fossil version of Zapdos isn't as powerful as the Basic set version. Fossil Zapdos has fewer hit points, one power instead of two, and its thunderstorm-based power is weaker than its lightning bolt-based power.

Zubat

Set: Fossil
Evolution: Into Golbat
Card Number: 57
Rarity: Common
English 1st Edition Price: $.50–$1
English 2nd Edition Price: $.25–$.50
Japanese Price: $.50–$1

A purple bat with no eyes, Zubat flies with a colony of other zubats. They navigate just like real bats—with sound waves that bounce off obstacles and tell them where to fly. Like Golbat, Zubat can suck the life out of its foes and heal itself in the process.

Trainer Cards

Energy Search

Set: Fossil
Card Number: 59
Rarity: Common
English 1st Edition Price: $.50–$1
English 2nd Edition Price: $.25–$.50
Japanese Price: $.50–$1

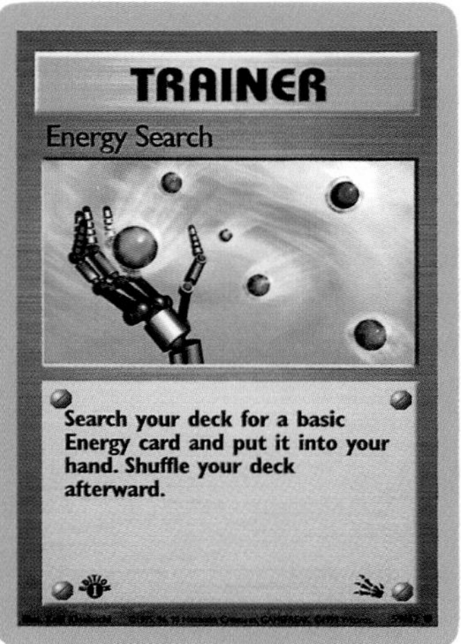

This is a great card for those pokémon who need more than one type of energy to attack and defend well.

Gambler

Set: Fossil
Card Number: 60
Rarity: Common
English 1st Edition Price: $.50–$1
English 2nd Edition Price: $.25–$.50
Japanese Price: $.50–$1

If you want to roll the dice and take a risk, this trainer card is for you. When you play it, you're gambling that you'll get something good, but you could get nothing.

Mr. Fuji

Set: Fossil
Card Number: 58
Rarity: Uncommon
English 1st Edition Price: $2.50–$3.50
English 2nd Edition Price: $1.25–$2.25
Japanese Price: $2.25–$3.50

You can tell from the picture that Mr. Fuji loves pokémon. In the game, he can protect endangered pokémon by returning them to your hand.

Mysterious Fossil

Set: Fossil
Evolution: Into Aerodactyl, Kabuto, Omanyte
Card Number: 62
Rarity: Common
English 1st Edition Price: $.50–$1
English 2nd Edition Price: $.25–$.50
Japanese Price: $.50–$1

This is the fossil from which Aerodactyl, Kabuto, and Omanyte all evolved.

Recycle

Set: Fossil
Card Number: 61
Rarity: Common
English 1st Edition Price: $.50–$1
English 2nd Edition Price: $.25–$.50
Japanese Price: $.50–$1

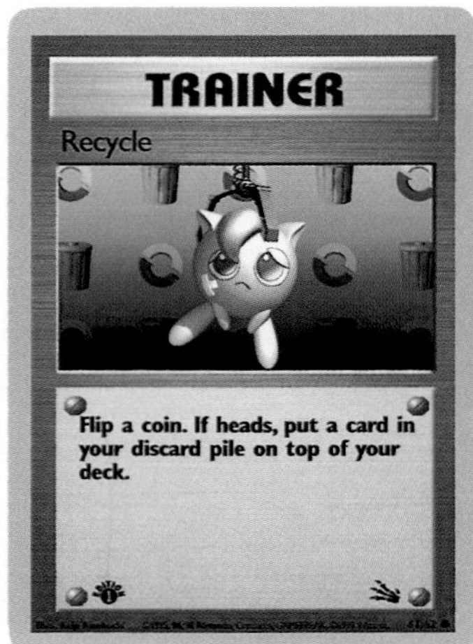

Just as we can recycle newspapers and cans, things can be recycled in the pokémon world. This is a powerful ability.

Team Rocket Expansion

64 Cards in Japanese Edition; 78 Cards in English First and Second Editions

Abra

Set: Team Rocket
Evolution: Into Bad Kadabra
Pokémon Number: 63
Rarity: Common
English 1st Edition Price: $.25–$.75
Japanese Price: $.50–$1

Abra would rather take a nap and be left alone than become involved in pokémon duels. And it is a good thing, as both its attacks are weak, doing no more than 10 points of damage. To make matters worse, it only takes 40 hit points, so it doesn't last long in battle. Why play it? Because it evolves into the awesome Alakazam!

Bad Alakazam

Set: Team Rocket
Evolution: From Bad Kadabra
Pokémon Number: 65
Rarity: Rare (Holofoil)
English 1st Edition Price: $8–$14
English 1st Edition Holofoil Price: $12–$20
Japanese Price: $12–$18

Bad Arbok

Set: Team Rocket
Evolution: From Bad Ekans
Pokémon Number: 24
Rarity: Rare (Holofoil)
English 1st Edition Price: $8–$12
English 1st Edition Holofoil Price: $14–$24
Japanese Price: $12–$18

This cobra is bad news, and it becomes even meaner in its "bad" Team Rocket version. Both its attacks can damage its opponent's pokémon, and not just the active ones, making it dangerous to those pocket monsters with special powers who like to sit on the bench where it's usually safe.

Seadra

Set: Fossil
Evolution: From Horsea
Card Number: 42
Rarity: Uncommon
English 1st Edition Price: $2.50–$3.50
English 2nd Edition Price: $1.25–$2.25
Japanese Price: $2.25–$3.50

Sea horses are charming in your fish tank, but what happens when you meet a 3-foot, 55-pound one in the wild? First you swim away, then you marvel at its incredible agility and accuracy with a water gun that can pound lesser pokémon into oblivion.

Shellder

Set: Fossil
Evolution: Into Cloyster
Card Number: 54
Rarity: Common
English 1st Edition Price: $.50–$1
English 2nd Edition Price: $.25–$.50
Japanese Price: $.50–$1

With only 30 hit points, Shellder seems very vulnerable, but it's not really. If it hides in its shell, it can't be harmed by any attack, whether it be a natural disaster or a menacing pokémon going nuclear on it. Should it decide to attack, it lets out a supersonic blast that can confuse other pokémon.

Slowbro

Set: Fossil
Evolution: From Slowpoke
Card Number: 43
Rarity: Uncommon
English 1st Edition Price: $2.50–$3.50
English 2nd Edition Price: $1.25–$2.25
Japanese Price: $2.25–$3.50

Slowbro looks a little odd—it's a pink bear with a living conch shell clamped onto its tail. How did it get that way? Slowbro loves to fish with its tail, and one day a hermit crab latched onto its tail and decided to stay. Slowbro could actually be related to Alakazam; it has a damage-absorbing ability very similar to Alakazam's.

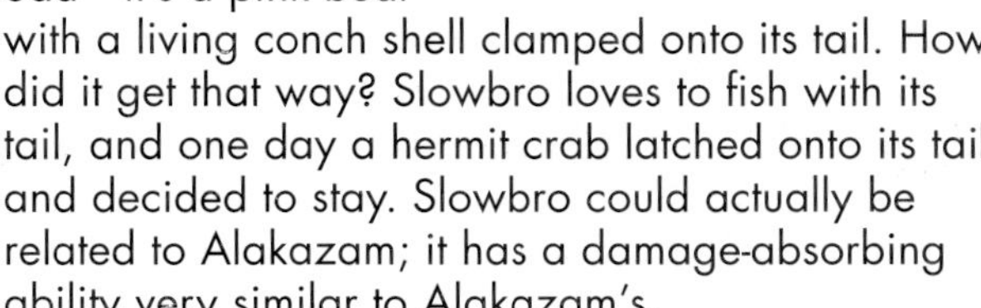

Slowpoke

Set: Fossil
Evolution: Into Slowbro
Card Number: 55
Rarity: Common
English 1st Edition Price: $.50–$1
English 2nd Edition Price: $.25–$.50
Japanese Price: $.50–$1

This dopey pokémon's picture looks like an animation out of *The Simpsons* TV show, and, appropriately enough, you can't take it very seriously. It can't fight at all—it can only take a beating and retrieve a trainer card from the discard pile by expending psychic energy. We feel bad for Slowpoke; that's why he's in our collection.

Tentacool

Set: Fossil
Evolution: Into Tentacruel
Card Number: 56
Rarity: Common
English 1st Edition Price: $.50–$1
English 2nd Edition Price: $.25–$.50
Japanese Price: $.50–$1

Tentacool is really timid: It doesn't like to fight other pokémon, but, if it does, it can defend itself with a special acid it releases into the water. In game terms, Tentacool has the neat ability to jump back into your hand from play any time during your turn to protect itself.

Weezing

Set: Fossil
Evolution: From Koffing
Card Number: 45
Rarity: Uncommon
English 1st Edition Price: $2.50–$3.50
English 2nd Edition Price: $1.25–$2.25
Japanese Price: $2.25–$3.50

When two stars meet, they fuse together to make a bigger star. Same thing happens with two koffings: When their poison gases mix together, they gradually metamorph into a weezing. This poison gas pokémon can let loose a smog attack and can explode, suffocating other pokémon in the area.

Tentacruel

Set: Fossil
Evolution: From Tentacool
Card Number: 44
Rarity: Uncommon
English 1st Edition Price: $2.50–$3.50
English 2nd Edition Price: $1.25–$2.25
Japanese Price: $2.25–$3.50

The crueler evolution of Tentacool has 12 different jellyfishlike tentacles that can sting enemy pokémon and poison them. Unlike most jellyfish, it's not transparent, so you can see this 120-pound monster coming. Trainers who want to capture a tentacruel would be wise to knock it out with a lightning pokémon.

Zapdos

Set: Fossil
Evolution: None
Card Number: 30/Holofoil #15
Rarity: Rare
English 1st Edition Holofoil Price: $8–$16
English 1st Edition Regular Price: $6–$10
English 2nd Edition Holofoil Price: $8–$14
English 2nd Edition Regular Price: $5–$8
Japanese Price: $15–$20

It may look like Big Bird getting shocked, but it's not—it's Zapdos, the largest electric pokémon in the game. The Fossil version of Zapdos isn't as powerful as the Basic set version. Fossil Zapdos has fewer hit points, one power instead of two, and its thunderstorm-based power is weaker than its lightning bolt-based power.

Zubat

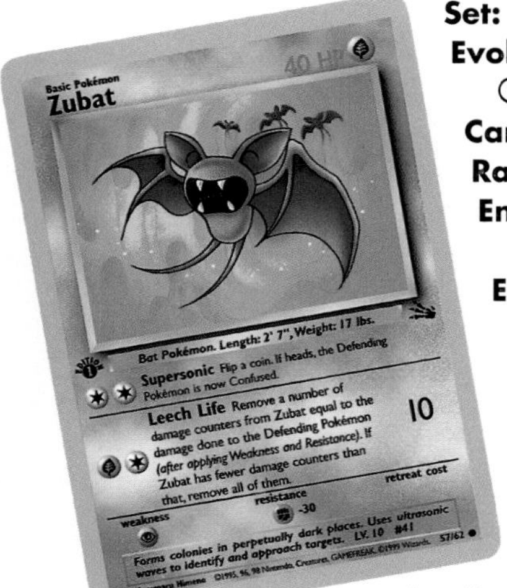

Set: Fossil
Evolution: Into Golbat
Card Number: 57
Rarity: Common
English 1st Edition Price: $.50–$1
English 2nd Edition Price: $.25–$.50
Japanese Price: $.50–$1

A purple bat with no eyes, Zubat flies with a colony of other zubats. They navigate just like real bats—with sound waves that bounce off obstacles and tell them where to fly. Like Golbat, Zubat can suck the life out of its foes and heal itself in the process.

TRAINER CARDS

Energy Search

Set: Fossil
Card Number: 59
Rarity: Common
English 1st Edition Price: $.50–$1
English 2nd Edition Price: $.25–$.50
Japanese Price: $.50–$1

This is a great card for those pokémon who need more than one type of energy to attack and defend well.

Gambler

Set: Fossil
Card Number: 60
Rarity: Common
English 1st Edition Price: $.50–$1
English 2nd Edition Price: $.25–$.50
Japanese Price: $.50–$1

If you want to roll the dice and take a risk, this trainer card is for you. When you play it, you're gambling that you'll get something good, but you could get nothing.

Mr. Fuji

Set: Fossil
Card Number: 58
Rarity: Uncommon
English 1st Edition Price: $2.50–$3.50
English 2nd Edition Price: $1.25–$2.25
Japanese Price: $2.25–$3.50

You can tell from the picture that Mr. Fuji loves pokémon. In the game, he can protect endangered pokémon by returning them to your hand.

Mysterious Fossil

Set: Fossil
Evolution: Into Aerodactyl, Kabuto, Omanyte
Card Number: 62
Rarity: Common
English 1st Edition Price: $.50–$1
English 2nd Edition Price: $.25–$.50
Japanese Price: $.50–$1

This is the fossil from which Aerodactyl, Kabuto, and Omanyte all evolved.

Recycle

Set: Fossil
Card Number: 61
Rarity: Common
English 1st Edition Price: $.50–$1
English 2nd Edition Price: $.25–$.50
Japanese Price: $.50–$1

Just as we can recycle newspapers and cans, things can be recycled in the poké-mon world. This is a powerful ability.

Team Rocket Expansion

64 Cards in Japanese Edition; 78 Cards in English First and Second Editions

Abra

Set: Team Rocket
Evolution: Into Bad Kadabra
Pokémon Number: 63
Rarity: Common
English 1st Edition Price: $.25–$.75
Japanese Price: $.50–$1

Abra would rather take a nap and be left alone than become involved in pokémon duels. And it is a good thing, as both its attacks are weak, doing no more than 10 points of damage. To make matters worse, it only takes 40 hit points, so it doesn't last long in battle. Why play it? Because it evolves into the awesome Alakazam!

Bad Alakazam

Set: Team Rocket
Evolution: From Bad Kadabra
Pokémon Number: 65
Rarity: Rare (Holofoil)
English 1st Edition Price: $8–$14
English 1st Edition Holofoil Price: $12–$20
Japanese Price: $12–$18

Bad Arbok

Set: Team Rocket
Evolution: From Bad Ekans
Pokémon Number: 24
Rarity: Rare (Holofoil)
English 1st Edition Price: $8–$12
English 1st Edition Holofoil Price: $14–$24
Japanese Price: $12–$18

This cobra is bad news, and it becomes even meaner in its "bad" Team Rocket version. Both its attacks can damage its opponent's pokémon, and not just the active ones, making it dangerous to those pocket monsters with special powers who like to sit on the bench where it's usually safe.

Bad Blastoise

Set: Team Rocket
Evolution: From Bad Wartortle
Pokémon Number: 9
Rarity: Rare (Holofoil)
English 1st Edition Price: $12–$20
English 1st Edition Holofoil Price: $18–$26
Japanese Price: $18–$25

Bad Charizard

Set: Team Rocket
Evolution: From Bad Charmeleon
Pokémon Number: 6
Rarity: Rare (Holofoil)
English 1st Edition Price: $14–$24
English 1st Edition Holofoil Price: $25–$45
Japanese Price: $30–$36

Bad Charmeleon

Set: Team Rocket
Evolution: From Bad Charmander/Into Bad Charizard
Pokémon Number: 5
Rarity: Uncommon
English 1st Edition Price: $1.50–$3.50
Japanese Price: $1.50–$3.50

Bad Dragonair

Set: Team Rocket
Evolution: From Bad Dratini/Into Bad Dragonite
Pokémon Number: 148
Rarity: Uncommon
English 1st Edition Price: $2–$4
Japanese Price: $3–$8

Bad Dragonite

Set: Team Rocket
Evolution: From Bad Dragonair
Pokémon Number: 149
Rarity: Rare (Holofoil)
English 1st Edition Price: $10–$16
English 1st Edition Holofoil Price: $18–$30
Japanese Price: $16–$24

Bad Dugtrio

Set: Team Rocket
Evolution: From Bad Diglett
Pokémon Number: 51
Rarity: Rare (Holofoil)
English 1st Edition Price: $6–$12
English 1st Edition Holofoil Price: $15–$20
Japanese Price: $12–$16

Bad Electrode

Set: Team Rocket
Evolution: From Bad Voltorb
Pokémon Number: 101
Rarity: Uncommon
English 1st Edition Price: $1.50–$3.50
Japanese Price: $1.50–$4

Bad Flareon

Set: Team Rocket
Evolution: From Bad Eevee
Pokémon Number: 136
Rarity: Uncommon
English 1st Edition Price: $1.50–$3.50
Japanese Price: $2–$5

Bad Gloom

Set: Team Rocket
Evolution: From Bad Oddish
Pokémon Number: 44
Rarity: Uncommon
English 1st Edition Price: $1.50–$3.50
Japanese Price: $2.50–$5

Bad Golbat

Set: Team Rocket
Evolution: From Bad Zubat
Pokémon Number: 42
Rarity: Rare (Holofoil)
English 1st Edition Price: $6–$12
English 1st Edition Holofoil Price: $14–$18
Japanese Price: $9–$14

Bad Golduck

Set: Team Rocket
Evolution: From Bad Psyduck
Pokémon Number: 55
Rarity: Uncommon
English 1st Edition Price: $1.50–$3.50
Japanese Price: $1.50–$4

Bad Gyarados

Set: Team Rocket
Evolution: From Bad Magikarp
Pokémon Number: 130
Rarity: Rare (Holofoil)
English 1st Edition Price: $8–$14
English 1st Edition Holofoil Price: $18–$28
Japanese Price: $13–$19

Bad Hypno

Set: Team Rocket
Evolution: From Bad Drowzee
Pokémon Number: 97
Rarity: Rare (Holofoil)
English 1st Edition Price: $8–$14
English 1st Edition Holofoil Price: $16–$22
Japanese Price: $12–$18

Bad Jolteon

Set: Team Rocket
Evolution: From Bad Eevee
Pokémon Number: 135
Rarity: Uncommon
English 1st Edition Price: $1.50–$3.50
Japanese Price: $2–$5

Bad Kadabra

Set: Team Rocket
Evolution: From Bad Abra/Into Bad Alakazam
Pokémon Number: 64
Rarity: Uncommon
English 1st Edition Price: $1.50–$3.50
Japanese Price: $1.50–$4

Bad versions of pokémon are the result of Team Rocket scientists cloning existing pokémon. They did this to breed stronger pokémon, but instead they made meaner ones. This meaner Kadabra gains the pokémon power "Barter," which allows its owner to discard a card from his or her hand and draw a new one. Not bad.

Bad Machamp

Set: Team Rocket
Evolution: From Bad Machoke
Pokémon Number: 68
Rarity: Rare (Holofoil)
English 1st Edition Price: $6–$12
English 1st Edition Holofoil Price: $15–$20
Japanese Price: $12–$18

Bad Machoke

Set: Team Rocket
Evolution: From Bad Machop/Into Bad Machamp
Pokémon Number: 67
Rarity: Uncommon
English 1st Edition Price: $1.50–$3.50
Japanese Price: $1.50–$4

Bad Magneton

Set: Team Rocket
Evolution: From Bad Magnemite
Pokémon Number: 82
Rarity: Rare (Holofoil)
English 1st Edition Price: $8–$14
English 1st Edition Holofoil Price: $16–$22
Japanese Price: $13–$17

Bad Muk

Set: Team Rocket
Evolution: From Bad Grimer
Pokémon Number: 89
Rarity: Uncommon
English 1st Edition Price: $2–$4
Japanese Price: $1.50–$4

Bad Persian

Set: Team Rocket
Evolution: From Bad Meowth
Pokémon Number: 53
Rarity: Common
English 1st Edition Price: $.25–$.75
Japanese Price: $.50–$1

Bad Primeape

Set: Team Rocket
Evolution: From Bad Mankey
Pokémon Number: 57
Rarity: Uncommon
English 1st Edition Price: $1.50–$3.50
Japanese Price: $1.50–$4

Bad Rapidash

Set: Team Rocket
Evolution: From Bad Ponyta
Pokémon Number: 78
Rarity: Common
English 1st Edition Price: $.25–$.75
Japanese Price: $.50–$1

Bad Raticate

Set: Team Rocket
Evolution: From Bad Rattata
Pokémon Number: 20
Rarity: Common
English 1st Edition Price: $.25–$.75
Japanese Price: $.50–$1

Bad Slowbro

Set: Team Rocket
Evolution: From Bad Slowpoke
Pokémon Number: 80
Rarity: Rare (Holofoil)
English 1st Edition Price: $6–$12
English 1st Edition Holofoil Price: $14–$18
Japanese Price: $12–$16

Bad Vaporeon

Set: Team Rocket
Evolution: From Bad Eevee
Pokémon Number: 134
Rarity: Uncommon
English 1st Edition Price: $1.50–$3.50
Japanese Price: $2.50–$6

Bad Vileplume

Set: Team Rocket
Evolution: From Bad Gloom
Pokémon Number: 45
Rarity: Rare (Holofoil)
English 1st Edition Price: $6–$12
English 1st Edition Holofoil Price: $15–$20
Japanese Price: $12–$18

Bad Wartortle

Set: Team Rocket
Evolution: From Bad Squirtle/Into Bad Blastoise
Pokémon Number: 8
Rarity: Uncommon
English 1st Edition Price: $1.50–$3.50
Japanese Price: $2.50–$5

Bad Weezing

Set: Team Rocket
Evolution: From Bad Koffing
Pokémon Number: 110
Rarity: Rare (Holofoil)
English 1st Edition Price: $6–$12
English 1st Edition Holofoil Price: $16–$22
Japanese Price: $12–$18

Usually the average pokémon deals about 20 to 30 damage for a two-energy attack. Forget that for Bad Weezing—it has the potential to deal 240 points of damage! Count up all the koffings, weezings, and bad weezings in play and your attacking Bad Weezing deals 20 times that amount. Awesome!

Charmander

Set: Team Rocket
Evolution: Into Charmeleon
Pokémon Number: 4
Rarity: Common
English 1st Edition Price: $.25–$.75
Japanese Price: $.50–$1

Diglett

Set: Team Rocket
Evolution: Into Dugtrio
Pokémon Number: 50
Rarity: Common
English 1st Edition Price: $.25–$.75
Japanese Price: $.50–$1

Dratini

Set: Team Rocket
Evolution: Into Dragonair
Pokémon Number: 147
Rarity: Common
English 1st Edition Price: $.25–$.75
Japanese Price: $.50–$1

Drowzee

Set: Team Rocket
Evolution: Into Hypno
Pokémon Number: 96
Rarity: Common
English 1st Edition Price: $.25–$.75
Japanese Price: $.50–$1

Eevee

Set: Team Rocket
Evolution: Into Flareon, Jolteon, Vaporeon
Pokémon Number: 133
Rarity: Common
English 1st Edition Price: $.25–$.75
Japanese Price: $.50–$1

Ekans

Set: Team Rocket
Evolution: Into Arbok
Pokémon Number: 23
Rarity: Common
English 1st Edition Price: $.25–$.75
Japanese Price: $.50–$1

Grimer

Set: Team Rocket
Evolution: Into Muk
Pokémon Number: 88
Rarity: Common
English 1st Edition Price: $.25–$.75
Japanese Price: $.50–$1

Most pokémon are lucky to either have poison or paralyzation attacks, but Grimer has both. For only one grass energy, Grimer can automatically poison the defender. For two green energy, it deals 10 damage and, if you win the coin flip, adds an additional 20 damage and paralyzation. Not bad for a basic pokémon.

Koffing

Set: Team Rocket
Evolution: Into Weezing
Pokémon Number: 109
Rarity: Common
English 1st Edition Price: $.25–$.75
Japanese Price: $.50–$1

Machop

Set: Team Rocket
Evolution: Into Machoke
Pokémon Number: 66
Rarity: Common
English 1st Edition Price: $.25–$.75
Japanese Price: $.50–$1

Magikarp

Set: Team Rocket
Evolution: Into Gyarados
Pokémon Number: 129
Rarity: Common
English 1st Edition Price: $.25–$.75
Japanese Price: $.50–$1

Magnemite

Set: Team Rocket
Evolution: Into Magneton
Pokémon Number: 81
Rarity: Common
English 1st Edition Price: $.25–$.75
Japanese Price: $.50–$1

Mankey

Set: Team Rocket
Evolution: Into Primeape
Pokémon Number: 56
Rarity: Common
English 1st Edition Price: $.25–$.75
Japanese Price: $.50–$1

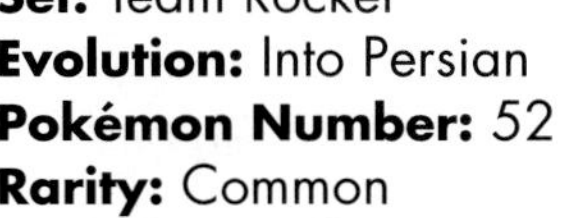

Meowth

Set: Team Rocket
Evolution: Into Persian
Pokémon Number: 52
Rarity: Common
English 1st Edition Price: $.25–$.75
Japanese Price: $.50–$1

Oddish

Set: Team Rocket
Evolution: Into Gloom
Pokémon Number: 43
Rarity: Common
English 1st Edition Price: $.25–$.75
Japanese Price: $.50–$1

Ponyta

Set: Team Rocket
Evolution: Into Rapidash
Pokémon Number: 77
Rarity: Common
English 1st Edition Price: $.25–$.75
Japanese Price: $.50–$1

Porygon

Set: Team Rocket
Evolution: None
Pokémon Number: 137
Rarity: Common
English 1st Edition Price: $.25–$.75
Japanese Price: $.50–$1

Psyduck

Set: Team Rocket
Evolution: Into Golduck
Pokémon Number: 54
Rarity: Common
English 1st Edition Price: $.25–$.75
Japanese Price: $.50–$1

Rattata

Set: Team Rocket
Evolution: Into Raticate
Pokémon Number: 19
Rarity: Common
English 1st Edition Price: $.25–$.75
Japanese Price: $.50–$1

The Team Rocket set doesn't help everyone's second favorite mouse much. Though it now has the pokémon power "Make Mischief," that power only allows you to swap prize cards with the top card from your deck. Since you don't usually know what you're swapping, it's a pretty useless power.

Slowpoke

Set: Team Rocket
Evolution: Into Slowbro
Pokémon Number: 79
Rarity: Common
English 1st Edition Price: $.25–$.75
Japanese Price: $.50–$1

Squirtle

Set: Team Rocket
Evolution: Into Wartortle
Pokémon Number: 7
Rarity: Common
English 1st Edition Price: $.25–$.75
Japanese Price: $.50–$1

Voltorb

Set: Team Rocket
Evolution: Into Electrode
Pokémon Number: 100
Rarity: Common
English 1st Edition Price: $.25–$.75
Japanese Price: $.50–$1

Zubat

Set: Team Rocket
Evolution: Into Golbat
Pokémon Number: 41
Rarity: Common
English 1st Edition Price: $.25–$.75
Japanese Price: $.50–$1

Trainer Cards

Boss's Method

Set: Team Rocket
Rarity: Common
English 1st Edition Price: $.25–$.75
Japanese Price: $.50–$1

Colorless Energy Potion

Set: Team Rocket
Rarity: Common
English 1st Edition Price: $.25–$.75
Japanese Price: $.50–$1

Here Comes Team Rocket

Set: Team Rocket
Rarity: Ultra Rare (Holofoil)
English 1st Edition Holofoil Price: $50–$100
Japanese Price: $35–$75

Healing Colorless Energy

Set: Team Rocket
Rarity: Common
English 1st Edition Price: $.25–$.75
Japanese Price: $.50–$1

Imposter Oak's Revenge

Set: Team Rocket
Rarity: Uncommon
English 1st Edition Price: $1.50–$3.50
Japanese Price: $1.50–$4

Letter of Challenge

Set: Team Rocket
Rarity: Uncommon
English 1st Edition Price: $1.50–$3.50
Japanese Price: $1.50–$4

Nighttime Garbage Collection

Set: Team Rocket
Rarity: Common
English 1st Edition Price: $.25–$.75
Japanese Price: $.50–$1

Rainbow Energy

Set: Team Rocket
Rarity: Rare (Holofoil)
English 1st Edition Holofoil Price: $16–$24
Japanese Price: $14–$20

Rocket Girl

Set: Team Rocket
Rarity: Rare (Holofoil)
English 1st Edition Holofoil Price: $16–$24
Japanese Price: $10–$18

Sticky Gas

Set: Team Rocket
Rarity: Common
English 1st Edition Price: $.25–$.75
Japanese Price: $.50–$1

Sleep Team Rocket, Sleep

Set: Team Rocket
Rarity: Common
English 1st Edition Price: $.25–$.75
Japanese Price: $.50–$.75

The Battle Zone Has Craters

Set: Team Rocket
Rarity: Common
English 1st Edition Price: $.25–$.75
Japanese Price: $.50–$1

Note: To more easily find your favorite pokémon, all Gym Leaders cards are organized by pokémon number, from lowest to highest. See page 94 for a listing of all pokémon by their numbers.

Gym Leaders Preconstructed Decks

Gym Leaders introduced the concept of preconstructed decks based on individual trainers. Six different such decks have been released in Japan. Each contains the same number of cards in exactly the same mix. The Gym Leaders 1 and 2 expansions duplicate some of the cards in the preconstructed decks, though not all of them. Each deck contains a trainer card with the respective trainer's name on it and a "gym" card. These trainers can also be found in the expansion sets, though the ones in the decks are holofoil and the ones in the expansions are not. The "gym" cards trigger special "stadium" rules, which are simple and come included with the decks. The cards are available only by purchasing the respective preconstructed decks listed in this section. (In this section, we have only listed cards that are not repeated in Gym Leaders 1 and 2 expansion decks.)

The six decks are based on the following trainers and have the following themes.

Trainer's English Name	Trainer's Japanese Name	Primary Pokémon Type
Deck #1: Brock (Nivi City Gym)	Takeshi	Fighting
Deck #2: Misty (Hanada City)	Kasumi	Water
Deck #3: Lt. Surge (Kuchiba City)	Machisu	Lightning
Deck #4: Erica (Tamamushi City)	Erika	Grass
Deck #5: Sabrina (Yamabuki City)	Natsume	Psychic
Deck #6: Blaine (Gurentown)	Katsura	Fire
In Gym 2 Expansion Only: Giovanni	Sakaki	Grass/Fighting
In Gym 2 Expansion Only: Koga	Kyou	Grass

Deck #1

Brock's Sandshrew

Set: Gym Deck #1
Evolution: Into Sandslash
Pokémon Number: 27
Rarity: Fixed
Japanese Price: $.50–$1

Brock's Sandslash

Set: Gym Deck #1
Evolution: From Sandshrew
Pokémon Number: 28
Rarity: Fixed
Japanese Price: $2–$4

Brock's Zubat

Set: Gym Deck #1
Evolution: Into Golbat
Pokémon Number: 37
Rarity: Fixed
Japanese Price: $2–$4

Brock's Mankey

Set: Gym Deck #1
Evolution: Into Primeape
Pokémon Number: 56
Rarity: Fixed
Japanese Price: $.50–$1

Brock's Geodude

Set: Gym Deck #1
Evolution: Into Graveler
Pokémon Number: 74
Rarity: Fixed
Japanese Price: $2–$4

Brock's Graveler

Set: Gym Deck #1
Evolution: From Geodude/Into Golem
Pokémon Number: 75
Rarity: Fixed
Japanese Price: $2–$4

Brock's Onix

Set: Gym Deck #1
Evolution: None
Pokémon Number: 95
Rarity: Fixed
Japanese Price: $5–$8

Brock's Rhyhorn

Set: Gym Deck #1
Evolution: Into Rhydon
Pokémon Number: 111
Rarity: Fixed
Japanese Price: $4–$6

Deck #2

Misty's Psyduck

Set: Gym Deck #2
Evolution: Into Golduck
Pokémon Number: 54
Rarity: Fixed
Japanese Price: $.50–$1

Misty's Poliwag

Set: Gym Deck #2
Evolution: Into Poliwhirl
Pokémon Number: 60
Rarity: Fixed
Japanese Price: $.50–$1

Misty's Tentacool

Set: Gym Deck #2
Evolution: Into Tentacruel
Pokémon Number: 72
Rarity: Fixed
Japanese Price: $2–$4

Misty's Seel

Set: Gym Deck #2
Evolution: Into Dewgong
Pokémon Number: 86
Rarity: Fixed
Japanese Price: $2–$4

Misty's Shellder

Set: Gym Deck #2
Evolution: Into Cloyster
Pokémon Number: 90
Rarity: Fixed
Japanese Price: $2–$4

Misty's Cloyster

Set: Gym Deck #2
Evolution: From Shellder
Pokémon Number: 91
Rarity: Fixed
Japanese Price: $2–$4

Misty's Goldeen

Set: Gym Deck #2
Evolution: Into Seaking
Pokémon Number: 118
Rarity: Fixed
Japanese Price: $2–$4

Misty's Seaking

Set: Gym Deck #2
Evolution: From Goldeen
Pokémon Number: 119
Rarity: Fixed
Japanese Price: $2–$4

Misty's Staryu

Set: Gym Deck #2
Evolution: Into Starmie
Pokémon Number: 120
Rarity: Fixed
Japanese Price: $4–$6

Misty's Starmie

Set: Gym Deck #2
Evolution: From Staryu
Pokémon Number: 121
Rarity: Fixed
Japanese Price: $4–$6

Deck #3

Lt. Surge's Rattata

Set: Gym Deck #3
Evolution: Into Raticate
Pokémon Number: 19
Rarity: Fixed
Japanese Price: $.50–$1

Lt. Surge's Raticate

Set: Gym Deck #3
Evolution: From Rattata
Pokémon Number: 20
Rarity: Fixed
Japanese Price: $2–$4

Lt. Surge's Spearow

Set: Gym Deck #3
Evolution: Into Fearow
Pokémon Number: 21
Rarity: Fixed
Japanese Price: $.50–$1

Lt. Surge's Pikachu

Set: Gym Deck #3
Evolution: Into Raichu
Pokémon Number: 25 (50 hit points)
Rarity: Fixed
Japanese Price: $2–$4

Lt. Surge's Raichu

Set: Gym Deck #3
Evolution: From Pikachu
Pokémon Number: 26
Rarity: Fixed
Japanese Price: $10–$15

Lt. Surge's Voltorb

Set: Gym Deck #3
Evolution: Into Electrode
Pokémon Number: 100
Rarity: Fixed
Japanese Price: $.50–$1

Lt. Surge's Electrode

Set: Gym Deck #3
Evolution: From Voltorb
Pokémon Number: 101
Rarity: Fixed
Japanese Price: $8–$12

Lt. Surge's Electabuzz

Set: Gym Deck #3
Evolution: None
Pokémon Number: 125
Rarity: Fixed
Japanese Price: $8–$12

Deck #4

Erica's Clefairy

Set: Gym Deck #4
Evolution: Into Clefable
Pokémon Number: 35
Rarity: Fixed
Japanese Price: $4–$6

Erica's Oddish

Set: Gym Deck #4
Evolution: Into Gloom
Pokémon Number: 43
Rarity: Fixed
Japanese Price: $.50–$1

Erica's Gloom

Set: Gym Deck #4
Evolution: From Oddish
Pokémon Number: 44
Rarity: Fixed
Japanese Price: $10–$14

Erica's Bellsprout

Set: Gym Deck #4
Evolution: Into Weepinbell
Pokémon Number: 69
Rarity: Fixed
Japanese Price: $8–$10

Erica's Weepinbell

Set: Gym Deck #4
Evolution: From Bellsprout/Into Victrebell
Pokémon Number: 70
Rarity: Fixed
Japanese Price: $4–$6

Erica's Exeggcute

Set: Gym Deck #4
Evolution: Into Exeggutor
Pokémon Number: 102
Rarity: Fixed
Japanese Price: $4–$6

Deck #5

Sabrina's Abra

Set: Gym Deck #5
Evolution: Into Kadabra
Pokémon Number: 63 (40 hit points)
Rarity: Fixed
Japanese Price: $.50–$1

Sabrina's Abra

Set: Gym Deck #5
Evolution: Into Kadabra
Pokémon Number: 63 (50 hit points)
Rarity: Fixed
Japanese Price: $.50–$1

Sabrina's Kadabra

Set: Gym Deck #5
Evolution: From Abra/Into Alakazam
Pokémon Number: 64
Rarity: Fixed
Japanese Price: $7–$9

Sabrina's Alakazam

Set: Gym Deck #5
Evolution: From Kadabra
Pokémon Number: 65
Rarity: Fixed
Japanese Price: $8–$12

Sabrina's Gastly

Set: Gym Deck #5
Evolution: Into Haunter
Pokémon Number: 92 (30 hit points)
Rarity: Fixed
Japanese Price: $2–$4

Sabrina's Gastly

Set: Gym Deck #5
Evolution: Into Haunter
Pokémon Number: 92 (50 hit points)
Rarity: Fixed
Japanese Price: $2–$4

Sabrina's Haunter

Set: Gym Deck #5
Evolution: From Gastly/Into Gengar
Pokémon Number: 93
Rarity: Fixed
Japanese Price: $4–$6

Sabrina's Gengar

Set: Gym Deck #5
Evolution: From Haunter
Pokémon Number: 94
Rarity: Fixed
Japanese Price: $10–$15

Sabrina's Drowzee

Set: Gym Deck #5
Evolution: Into Hypno
Pokémon Number: 96
Rarity: Fixed
Japanese Price: $2–$4

Sabrina's Hypno

Set: Gym Deck #5
Evolution: From Drowzee
Pokémon Number: 97
Rarity: Fixed
Japanese Price: $2–$4

Sabrina's Mr. Mime

Set: Gym Deck #5
Evolution: None
Pokémon Number: 122
Rarity: Fixed
Japanese Price: $4–$6

Sabrina's Jynx

Set: Gym Deck #5
Evolution: None
Pokémon Number: 124
Rarity: Fixed
Japanese Price: $.50–$1

Sabrina's Porygon

Set: Gym Deck #5
Evolution: None
Pokémon Number: 137
Rarity: Fixed
Japanese Price: $.50–$1

Trainer Card

Master Ball

Set: Gym Deck #5
Rarity: Fixed
Japanese Price: $.50–$1

Deck #6

Blaine's Charmander

Set: Gym Deck #6
Evolution: Into Charmeleon
Pokémon Number: 4
Rarity: Fixed
Japanese Price: $3–$5

Blaine's Vulpix

Set: Gym Deck #6
Evolution: Into Ninetales
Pokémon Number: 37 (40 hit points)
Rarity: Fixed
Japanese Price: $.50–$1

Blaine's Vulpix

Set: Gym Deck #6
Evolution: Into Ninetales
Pokémon Number: 37 (50 hit points)
Rarity: Fixed
Japanese Price: $.50–$1

Blaine's Ninetales

Set: Gym Deck #6
Evolution: From Vulpix
Pokémon Number: 38
Rarity: Fixed
Japanese Price: $9–$12

Blaine's Growlithe

Set: Gym Deck #6
Evolution: Into Arcanine
Pokémon Number: 58 (50 hit points)
Rarity: Fixed
Japanese Price: $.50–$1

Blaine's Growlithe

Set: Gym Deck #6
Evolution: Into Arcanine
Pokémon Number: 58 (60 hit points)
Rarity: Fixed
Japanese Price: $.50–$1

Blaine's Arcanine

Set: Gym Deck #6
Evolution: From Growlithe
Pokémon Number: 59
Rarity: Fixed
Japanese Price: $7–$10

Blaine's Ponyta

Set: Gym Deck #6
Evolution: Into Rapidash
Pokémon Number: 77 (40 hit points)
Rarity: Fixed
Japanese Price: $2–$4

Blaine's Ponyta

Set: Gym Deck #6
Evolution: Into Rapidash
Pokémon Number: 77 (50 hit points)
Rarity: Fixed
Japanese Price: $2–$4

Blaine's Rapidash

Set: Gym Deck #6
Evolution: From Ponyta
Pokémon Number: 78
Rarity: Fixed
Japanese Price: $4–$6

Blaine's Doduo

Set: Gym Deck #6
Evolution: Into Dodrio
Pokémon Number: 84
Rarity: Fixed
Japanese Price: $.50–$1

Blaine's Dodrio

Set: Gym Deck #6
Evolution: From Doduo
Pokémon Number: 85
Rarity: Fixed
Japanese Price: $4–$6

Blaine's Magmar

Set: Gym Deck #6
Evolution: None
Pokémon Number: 126
Rarity: Fixed
Japanese Price: $5–$8

Trainer Cards

Blaine's Quiz One

Set: Gym Deck #6
Rarity: Fixed
Japanese Price: $2–$4

Blaine's Quiz Two

Set: Gym Deck #6
Rarity: Fixed
Japanese Price: $.50–$1

Health Crystal

Set: Gym Deck #6
Rarity: Fixed
Japanese Price: $.50–$1

Hot-Blooded

Set: Gym Deck #6
Rarity: Fixed
Japanese Price: $.50–$1

Gym Leaders Expansion 1

Erica's Bulbasaur

Set: Gym Leaders 1
Evolution: Into Ivysaur
Pokémon Number: 1
Rarity: Uncommon
Japanese Price: $2.50–$5

Lt. Surge's Rattata

Set: Gym Leaders 1
Evolution: Into Raticate
Pokémon Number: 19
Rarity: Common
Japanese Price: $.50–$1

Lt. Surge's Raticate

Set: Gym Leaders 1
Evolution: From Rattata
Pokémon Number: 20
Rarity: Uncommon
Japanese Price: $2.50–$5

For only two energy, this Raticate has one of the most potent pokémon powers in the game. If you spend one turn storing up energy from its first power, its second power can deal a whopping 80 damage to the defending pokémon. Plus, psychic pokémon have a hard time hurting Raticate because of its resistance.

Lt. Surge's Spearow

Set: Gym Leaders 1
Evolution: Into Fearow
Pokémon Number: 21
Rarity: Common
Japanese Price: $.50–$1

Lt. Surge's Fearow

Set: Gym Leaders 1
Evolution: From Spearow
Pokémon Number: 22
Rarity: Rare
Japanese Price: $8–$12

Lt. Surge's Pikachu

Set: Gym Leaders 1
Evolution: Into Raichu
Pokémon Number: 25 (40 hit points)
Rarity: Common
Japanese Price: $.50–$1

Brock's Sandshrew

Set: Gym Leaders 1
Evolution: Into Sandslash
Pokémon Number: 27
Rarity: Common
Japanese Price: $.50–$1

Brock's Sandslash

Set: Gym Leaders 1
Evolution: From Sandshrew
Pokémon Number: 28
Rarity: Uncommon
Japanese Price: $2.50–$5

Erica's Clefairy

Set: Gym Leaders 1
Evolution: Into Clefable
Pokémon Number: 35
Rarity: Uncommon
Japanese Price: $2.50–$5

Erica's Clefable

Set: Gym Leaders 1
Evolution: From Clefairy
Pokémon Number: 36
Rarity: Rare
Japanese Price: $13–$16

Brock's Vulpix

Set: Gym Leaders 1
Evolution: Into Ninetales
Pokémon Number: 37 (40 hit points)
Rarity: Common
Japanese Price: $.50–$1

Brock's Vulpix

Set: Gym Leaders 1
Evolution: Into Ninetales
Pokémon Number: 37 (50 hit points)
Rarity: Uncommon
Japanese Price: $2.50–$5

Brock's Ninetales

Set: Gym Leaders 1
Evolution: From Vulpix
Pokémon Number: 38
Rarity: Rare
Japanese Price: $10–$14

Erica's Jigglypuff

Set: Gym Leaders 1
Evolution: Into Wigglytuff
Pokémon Number: 39
Rarity: Common
Japanese Price: $.50–$1

Brock's Zubat

Set: Gym Leaders 1
Evolution: Into Golbat
Pokémon Number: 41
Rarity: Common
Japanese Price: $.50–$1

Brock's Golbat

Set: Gym Leaders 1
Evolution: From Zubat
Pokémon Number: 42
Rarity: Uncommon
Japanese Price: $2.50–$5

Erica's Oddish

Set: Gym Leaders 1
Evolution: Into Gloom
Pokémon Number: 43 (40 hit points)
Rarity: Common
Japanese Price: $.50–$1

Erica's Oddish

Set: Gym Leaders 1
Evolution: Into Gloom
Pokémon Number: 43 (50 hit points)
Rarity: Common
Japanese Price: $.50–$1

Erica's Gloom

Set: Gym Leaders 1
Evolution: From Oddish/Into Vileplume
Pokémon Number: 44
Rarity: Uncommon
Japanese Price: $2.50–$5

Erica's Vileplume

Set: Gym Leaders 1
Evolution: From Gloom
Pokémon Number: 45
Rarity: Rare
Japanese Price: $10–$13

Erica's Paras

Set: Gym Leaders 1
Evolution: Into Parasect
Pokémon Number: 46
Rarity: Common
Japanese Price: $.50–$1

Brock's Diglett

Set: Gym Leaders 1
Evolution: Into Dugtrio
Pokémon Number: 50
Rarity: Common
Japanese Price: $.50–$1

Misty's Psyduck

Set: Gym Leaders 1
Evolution: Into Golduck
Pokémon Number: 54
Rarity: Common
Japanese Price: $.50–$1

For a basic pokémon, Misty's Psyduck has a lot of hit points with 60 and a very powerful ability that only uses one psychic energy. Its ability allows it to do three different things—draw an extra card, deal 20 damage to an opposing pokémon, and steal an opposing pokémon's power and use it for its own.

 Misty's Golduck 

Set: Gym Leaders 1
Evolution: From Psyduck
Pokémon Number: 55
Rarity: Rare
Japanese Price: $12–$15

 Brock's Mankey 

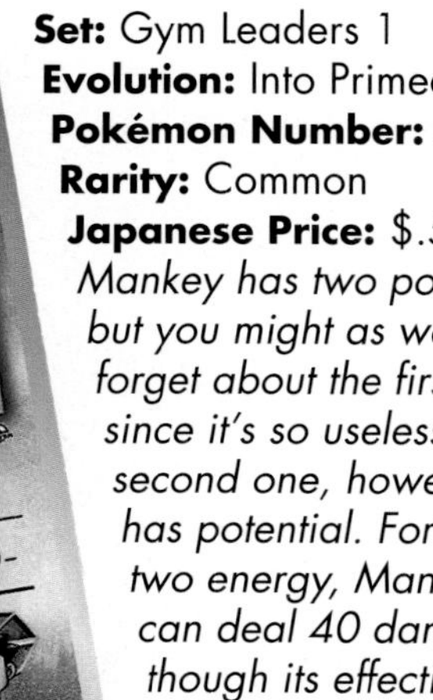

Set: Gym Leaders 1
Evolution: Into Primeape
Pokémon Number: 56
Rarity: Common
Japanese Price: $.50–$1

Mankey has two powers, but you might as well forget about the first one since it's so useless. The second one, however, has potential. For just two energy, Mankey can deal 40 damage, though its effectiveness will reduce as Mankey gets weaker. All things considered, this version is a better bargain than the Jungle Mankey.

 Brock's Primeape 

Set: Gym Leaders 1
Evolution: From Mankey
Pokémon Number: 57
Rarity: Uncommon
Japanese Price: $2.50–$5

 Misty's Poliwag 

Set: Gym Leaders 1
Evolution: Into Poliwhirl
Pokémon Number: 60
Rarity: Common
Japanese Price: $.50–$1

 Misty's Poliwhirl 

Set: Gym Leaders 1
Evolution: From Poliwag/Into Poliwrath
Pokémon Number: 61
Rarity: Uncommon
Japanese Price: $2.50–$5

 Erica's Bellsprout 

Set: Gym Leaders 1
Evolution: Into Weepinbell
Pokémon Number: 69 (40 hit points)
Rarity: Uncommon
Japanese Price: $2.50–$5

 Erica's Bellsprout 

Set: Gym Leaders 1
Evolution: Into Weepinbell
Pokémon Number: 69 (50 hit points)
Rarity: Common
Japanese Price: $.50–$1

 Erica's Weepinbell 

Set: Gym Leaders 1
Evolution: From Bellsprout/Into Victreebel
Pokémon Number: 70
Rarity: Uncommon
Japanese Price: $2.50–$5

 Erica's Victreebel 

Set: Gym Leaders 1
Evolution: From Weepinbell
Pokémon Number: 71
Rarity: Rare
Japanese Price: $8–$10

 Misty's Tentacool 

Set: Gym Leaders 1
Evolution: Into Tentacruel
Pokémon Number: 72
Rarity: Uncommon
Japanese Price: $2.50–$5

 Misty's Tentacruel 

Set: Gym Leaders 1
Evolution: From Tentacool
Pokémon Number: 73
Rarity: Rare
Japanese Price: $10–$13

Brock's Geodude

Set: Gym Leaders 1
Evolution: Into Graveler
Pokémon Number: 74 (40 hit points)
Rarity: Common
Japanese Price: $.50–$1

Brock's Geodude

Set: Gym Leaders 1
Evolution: Into Graveler
Pokémon Number: 74 (50 hit points)
Rarity: Common
Japanese Price: $.50–$1

Brock's Graveler

Set: Gym Leaders 1
Evolution: From Geodude/Into Golem
Pokémon Number: 75
Rarity: Uncommon
Japanese Price: $2.50–$5

Lt. Surge's Magnemite

Set: Gym Leaders 1
Evolution: Into Magneton
Pokémon Number: 81 (30 hit points)
Rarity: Uncommon
Japanese Price: $2.50–$5

Lt. Surge's Magnemite

Set: Gym Leaders 1
Evolution: Into Magneton
Pokémon Number: 81 (40 hit points)
Rarity: Common
Japanese Price: $.50–$1

Lt. Surge's Magneton

Set: Gym Leaders 1
Evolution: From Magnemite
Pokémon Number: 82
Rarity: Rare
Japanese Price: $10–$12

Misty's Seel

Set: Gym Leaders 1
Evolution: Into Dewgong

Pokémon Number: 86
Rarity: Common
Japanese Price: $.50–$1

It's rare to see a pokémon with two different attacks do exactly the same amount of damage, but that's what we have here with Seel. Its first attack does 10 damage and prevents the defending pokémon from retreating and running scared the next turn. The second attack also deals 10 and, with a successful coin flip, prevents the defender from attacking next turn.

Misty's Dewgong

Set: Gym Leaders 1
Evolution: From Seel
Pokémon Number: 87
Rarity: Uncommon
Japanese Price: $2.50–$5

Brock's Onix

Set: Gym Leaders 1
Evolution: None
Pokémon Number: 95
Rarity: Common
Japanese Price: $.50–$1

Lt. Surge's Voltorb

Set: Gym Leaders 1
Evolution: Into Electrode
Pokémon Number: 100
Rarity: Common
Japanese Price: $.50–$1

Erica's Exeggute

Set: Gym Leaders 1
Evolution: Into Exeggutor
Pokémon Number: 102
Rarity: Uncommon
Japanese Price: $2.50–$5

Erica's Exeggutor

Set: Gym Leaders 1
Evolution: From Exeggute
Pokémon Number: 103
Rarity: Uncommon
Japanese Price: $2.50–$5

Team Rocket's Hitmonchan

Set: Gym Leaders 1
Evolution: None
Pokémon Number: 107
Rarity: Rare
Japanese Price: $13–$17

Brock's Lickitung

Set: Gym Leaders 1
Evolution: None
Pokémon Number: 108
Rarity: Uncommon
Japanese Price: $2.50–$5

Brock's Rhyhorn

Set: Gym Leaders 1
Evolution: Into Rhydon
Pokémon Number: 111
Rarity: Common
Japanese Price: $.50–$1

Brock's Rhydon

Set: Gym Leaders 1
Evolution: From Rhyhorn
Pokémon Number: 112
Rarity: Rare
Japanese Price: $8–$10

Erica's Tangela

Set: Gym Leaders 1
Evolution: None
Pokémon Number: 114
Rarity: Common
Japanese Price: $.50–$1

Misty's Horsea

Set: Gym Leaders 1
Evolution: Into Seadra
Pokémon Number: 116 (40 hit points)
Rarity: Common
Japanese Price: $.50–$1

Misty's Horsea

Set: Gym Leaders 1
Evolution: Into Seadra
Pokémon Number: 116 (50 hit points)
Rarity: Common
Japanese Price: $.50–$1

Misty's Seadra

Set: Gym Leaders 1
Evolution: From Horsea
Pokémon Number: 117
Rarity: Rare
Japanese Price: $11–$13

Misty's Goldeen

Set: Gym Leaders 1
Evolution: Into Seaking
Pokémon Number: 118
Rarity: Common
Japanese Price: $.50–$1

Misty's Staryu

Set: Gym Leaders 1
Evolution: Into Starmie
Pokémon Number: 120
Rarity: Common
Japanese Price: $.50–$1

Team Rocket's Scyther

Set: Gym Leaders 1
Evolution: None
Pokémon Number: 123
Rarity: Rare
Japanese Price: $14–$18

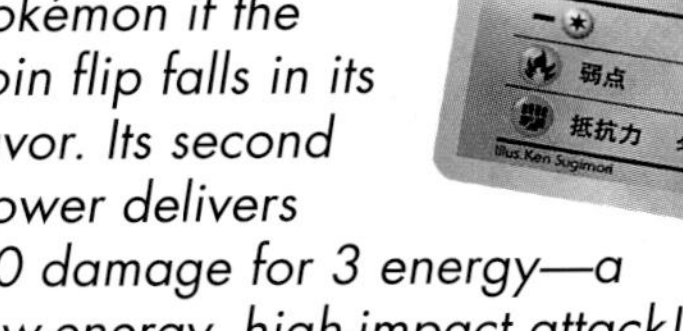

The Gym Leaders 1's Scyther is just as much a bruiser as the Jungle Scyther. For only one energy, it has a nifty defense that prevents it from receiving any damage from the attacking pokémon if the coin flip falls in its favor. Its second power delivers 40 damage for 3 energy—a low-energy, high-impact attack!

Lt. Surge's Electabuzz

Set: Gym Leaders 1
Evolution: None
Pokémon Number: 125
Rarity: Rare
Japanese Price: $12–$16

Misty's Magikarp

Set: Gym Leaders 1
Evolution: Into Gyarados
Pokémon Number: 129
Rarity: Common
Japanese Price: $.50–$1

Misty's Gyarados

Set: Gym Leaders 1
Evolution: From Magikarp
Pokémon Number: 130
Rarity: Rare
Japanese Price: $15–$20

Lt. Surge's Eevee

Set: Gym Leaders 1
Evolution: Into Flareon, Jolteon, Vaporean
Pokémon Number: 133
Rarity: Uncommon
Japanese Price: $2.50–$5

Lt. Surge's Jolteon

Set: Gym Leaders 1
Evolution: From Eevee
Pokémon Number: 135
Rarity: Rare
Japanese Price: $12–$16

Team Rocket's Moltres

Set: Gym Leaders 1
Evolution: None
Pokémon Number: 146
Rarity: Rare
Japanese Price: $14–$16

Erica's Dratini

Set: Gym Leaders 1
Evolution: Into Dragonair
Pokémon Number: 147
Rarity: Uncommon
Japanese Price: $2.50–$5

This pokémon has a special pokémon power that prevents it from taking more than 10 damage from any attack of 30 or greater. Ironically, for Dratini's "tail" attack you're looking for heads on the coin flip. If you get heads, the tail attack does 30, otherwise it deals a measly 10 damage.

Dragonair

Set: Gym Leaders 1
Evolution: From Dratini
Pokémon Number: 148
Rarity: Rare
Japanese Price: $13–$15

Trainer Cards

Brock

Set: Gym Leaders 1
Rarity: Rare
Japanese Price: $8–$10

Erica

Set: Gym Leaders 1
Rarity: Rare
Japanese Price: $6–$8

Lt. Surge

Set: Gym Leaders 1
Rarity: Rare
Japanese Price: $6–$8

Misty

Set: Gym Leaders 1
Rarity: Rare
Japanese Price: $6–$8

Misty's Game

Set: Gym Leaders 1
Rarity: Common
Japanese Price: $.50–$1

Misty's Tear

Set: Gym Leaders 1
Rarity: Common
Japanese Price: $.50–$1

Circulate Energy

Set: Gym Leaders 1
Rarity: Common
Japanese Price: $.50–$1

Misty's Anger

Set: Gym Leaders 1
Rarity: Uncommon
Japanese Price: $2.50–$5

Brock's Nurturing Style

Set: Gym Leaders 1
Rarity: Uncommon
Japanese Price: $2.50–$5

Make Recall

Set: Gym Leaders 1
Rarity: Uncommon
Japanese Price: $2.50–$5

Erica's Attendants

Set: Gym Leaders 1
Rarity: Uncommon
Japanese Price: $2.50–$5

Courteous Manners

Set: Gym Leaders 1
Rarity: Uncommon
Japanese Price: $2.50–$5

Erica's Perfume

Set: Gym Leaders 1
Rarity: Uncommon
Japanese Price: $2.50–$5

Lt. Surge's Negotiation

Set: Gym Leaders 1
Rarity: Uncommon
Japanese Price: $2.50–$5

Spy Operations

Set: Gym Leaders 1
Rarity: Uncommon
Japanese Price: $2.50–$5

Graceful Attack

Set: Gym Leaders 1
Rarity: Rare
Japanese Price: $5–$8

Team Rocket's Trap

Set: Gym Leaders 1
Rarity: Rare
Japanese Price: $7–$10

Lt. Surge's Secret Operation

Set: Gym Leaders 1
Rarity: Rare
Japanese Price: $5–$8

Brock's Protection

Set: Gym Leaders 1
Rarity: Rare
Japanese Price: $5–$7

Misty's Selfishness

Set: Gym Leaders 1
Rarity: Rare
Japanese Price: $5–$7

Erica's Kindness

Set: Gym Leaders 1
Rarity: Rare
Japanese Price: $5–$7

Hanada City Gym

Set: Gym Leaders 1
Rarity: Uncommon
Japanese Price: $2.50–$5

Kuchiba City Gym

Set: Gym Leaders 1
Rarity: Uncommon
Japanese Price: $2.50–$5

Nibi City Gym

Set: Gym Leaders 1
Rarity: Uncommon
Japanese Price: $2.50–$5

Tamamushi City Gym

Set: Gym Leaders 1
Rarity: Uncommon
Japanese Price: $2.50–$5

Remove Prohibition Gym

Set: Gym Leaders 1
Rarity: Rare
Japanese Price: $8–$10

Team Rocket's Special Training Gym

Set: Gym Leaders 1
Rarity: Rare
Japanese Price: $7–$9

Derangement Gym

Set: Gym Leaders 1
Rarity: Rare
Japanese Price: $5–$7

Narrow Gym

Set: Gym Leaders 1
Rarity: Rare
Japanese Price: $4–$6

Gym Leaders Expansion 2: Challenge From the Darkness

 Erica's Ivysaur 

Set: Gym Leaders 2
Evolution: From Bulbasaur/Into Venusaur
Pokémon Number: 2
Rarity: Uncommon
Japanese Price: $2.50–$5

 Erica's Venusaur 

Set: Gym Leaders 2
Evolution: From Ivysaur
Pokémon Number: 3
Rarity: Rare (Holofoil)
Japanese Price: $12–$16

 Blaine's Charmander 

Set: Gym Leaders 2
Evolution: Into Charmeleon
Pokémon Number: 4
Rarity: Common
Japanese Price: $.50–$1

 Blaine's Charmeleon 

Set: Gym Leaders 2
Evolution: From Charmander/Into Charizard
Pokémon Number: 5
Rarity: Uncommon
Japanese Price: $2.50–$5

 Blaine's Charizard 

Set: Gym Leaders 2
Evolution: From Charmeleon
Pokémon Number: 6
Rarity: Rare (Holofoil)
Japanese Price: $15–$25

 Koga's Weedle 

Set: Gym Leaders 2
Evolution: Into Kakuna
Pokémon Number: 13
Rarity: Common
Japanese Price: $.50–$1

 Koga's Kakuna 

Set: Gym Leaders 2
Evolution: From Weedle/Into Beedrill
Pokémon Number: 14
Rarity: Uncommon
Japanese Price: $2.50–$5

 Koga's Beedrill 

Set: Gym Leaders 2
Evolution: From Kakuna
Pokémon Number: 15
Rarity: Rare (Holofoil)
Japanese Price: $12–$16

 Koga's Pidgey (level 15) 

Set: Gym Leaders 2
Evolution: Into Pidgeotto
Pokémon Number: 16
Rarity: Common
Japanese Price: $.50–$1

Poor Koga, he got stuck with this cowardly pigeon. Its basic attack allows it to remove itself and all cards attached to it from the game and have them placed on top of your deck. While this may occasionally save it from being knocked out, it's a pretty rotten power.

 Koga's Pidgey (level 9) 

Set: Gym Leaders 2
Evolution: Into Pidgeotto
Pokémon Number: 16
Rarity: Uncommon
Japanese Price: $2.50–$5

 Koga's Pidgeotto 

Set: Gym Leaders 2
Evolution: From Pidgey
Pokémon Number: 17
Rarity: Rare
Japanese Price: $8–$12

 Koga's Ekans 

Set: Gym Leaders 2
Evolution: Into Arbok
Pokémon Number: 23
Rarity: Common
Japanese Price: $.50–$1

 Koga's Arbok 

Set: Gym Leaders 2
Evolution: From Ekans
Pokémon Number: 24
Rarity: Common
Japanese Price: $.50–$1

 Lt. Surge's Raichu 

Set: Gym Leaders 2
Evolution: From Pikachu
Pokémon Number: 26
Rarity: Rare (Holofoil)
Japanese Price: $15–$22

 Giovanni's Nidoran (female) 

Set: Gym Leaders 2
Evolution: Into Nidorina
Pokémon Number: 29
Rarity: Common
Japanese Price: $.50–$1

 Giovanni's Nidorina 

Set: Gym Leaders 2
Evolution: From Nidoran/Into Nidoqueen
Pokémon Number: 30
Rarity: Uncommon
Japanese Price: $2.50–$5

 Giovanni's Nidoqueen 

Set: Gym Leaders 2
Evolution: From Nidorina
Pokémon Number: 31
Rarity: Rare
Japanese Price: $8–$12

 Giovanni's Nidoran (male) 

Set: Gym Leaders 2
Evolution: Into Nidorino
Pokémon Number: 32
Rarity: Common
Japanese Price: $.50–$1

 Giovanni's Nidorino 

Set: Gym Leaders 2
Evolution: From Nidoran/Into Nidoking
Pokemon Number: 33
Rarity: Uncommon
Japanese Price: $2.50–$5

 Giovanni's Nidoking 

Set: Gym Leaders 2
Evolution: From Nidorino
Pokémon Number: 34
Rarity: Rare (Holofoil)
Japanese Price: $14–$18

Blaine's Vulpix

Set: Gym Leaders 2
Evolution: Into Ninetales
Pokémon Number: 37
Rarity: Common
Japanese Price: $.50–$1

Blaine's Ninetales

Set: Gym Leaders 2
Evolution: From Vulpix
Pokémon Number: 38
Rarity: Rare
Japanese Price: $8–$12

Koga's Zubat

Set: Gym Leaders 2
Evolution: Into Golbat
Pokémon Number: 41
Rarity: Common
Japanese Price: $.50–$1

Koga's Golbat

Set: Gym Leaders 2
Evolution: From Zubat
Pokémon Number: 42
Rarity: Uncommon
Japanese Price: $.50–$1

Sabrina's Venonat

Set: Gym Leaders 2
Evolution: Into Venomoth
Pokémon Number: 48
Rarity: Common
Japanese Price: $.50–$1

Sabrina's Venomoth

Set: Gym Leaders 2
Evolution: From Venonat
Pokémon Number: 49
Rarity: Rare
Japanese Price: $8–$12

Brock's Dugtrio

Set: Gym Leaders 2
Evolution: From Diglett
Pokémon Number: 51
Rarity: Rare
Japanese Price: $8–$12

Giovanni's Meowth (level 12)

Set: Gym Leaders 2
Evolution: Into Persian
Pokémon Number: 52
Rarity: Uncommon
Japanese Price: $2.50–$5

Giovanni's Meowth (level 17)

Set: Gym Leaders 2
Evolution: Into Persian
Pokémon Number: 52
Rarity: Common
Japanese Price:
$.50–$1

Meowth is all attitude with little ability, and this card proves it. While this bad kitty is always causing trouble for Ash and his friends, it's really not a good fighter. Both its attacks are average at best, though the first one can cause confusion for just one energy, which can be potent.

Giovanni's Persian

Set: Gym Leaders 2
Evolution: From Meowth
Pokémon Number: 53
Rarity: Rare (Holofoil)
Japanese Price: $12–$16

Sabrina's Psyduck

Set: Gym Leaders 2
Evolution: Into Golduck
Pokémon Number: 54
Rarity: Common
Japanese Price: $.50–$1

Sabrina's Golduck

Set: Gym Leaders 2
Evolution: From Psyduck
Pokémon Number: 55
Rarity: Rare
Japanese Price: $8–$12

Blaine's Mankey

Set: Gym Leaders 2
Evolution: Into Primeape
Pokémon Number: 56
Rarity: Common
Japanese Price: $.50–$1

Blaine's Growlithe

Set: Gym Leaders 2
Evolution: Into Arcanine
Pokémon Number: 58
Rarity: Common
Japanese Price: $.50–$1

Blaine's Arcanine

Set: Gym Leaders 2
Evolution: From Growlithe
Pokémon Number: 59
Rarity: Rare (Holofoil)
Japanese Price: $14–$18

Misty's Poliwrath

Set: Gym Leaders 2
Evolution: From Poliwhirl
Pokémon Number: 62
Rarity: Rare
Japanese Price: $8–$12

Sabrina's Abra

Set: Gym Leaders 2
Evolution: Into Kadabra
Pokémon Number: 63
Rarity: Common
Japanese Price: $.50–$1

Sabrina's Kadabra

Set: Gym Leaders 2
Evolution: From Abra/Into Alakazam
Pokémon Number: 64
Rarity: Uncommon
Japanese Price: $2.50–$5

Sabrina's Alakazam

Set: Gym Leaders 2
Evolution: From Kadabra
Pokémon Number: 65
Rarity: Rare (Holofoil)
Japanese Price: $15–$20

Giovanni's Machop

Set: Gym Leaders 2
Evolution: Into Machoke
Pokémon Number: 66
Rarity: Common
Japanese Price: $.50–$1

Giovanni's Machoke

Set: Gym Leaders 2
Evolution: From Machop/Into Machamp
Pokémon Number: 67
Rarity: Uncommon
Japanese Price: $2.50–$5

Giovanni's Machamp

Set: Gym Leaders 2
Evolution: From Machoke
Pokémon Number: 68
Rarity: Rare (Holofoil)
Japanese Price: $12–$16

 Blaine's Ponyta 

Set: Gym Leaders 2
Evolution: Into Rapidash
Pokémon Number: 77
Rarity: Common
Japanese Price: $.50–$1

 Blaine's Rapidash 

Set: Gym Leaders 2
Evolution: From Ponyta
Pokémon Number: 78
Rarity: Uncommon
Japanese Price: $2.50–$5

 Sabrina's Slowpoke 

Set: Gym Leaders 2
Evolution: Into Slowbro
Pokémon Number: 79
Rarity: Common
Japanese Price: $.50–$1

 Sabrina's Slowbro 

Set: Gym Leaders 2
Evolution: From Slowpoke
Pokémon Number: 80
Rarity: Uncommon
Japanese Price: $2.50–$5

 Imakuni's Doduo 

Set: Gym Leaders 2
Evolution: Into Dodrio
Pokémon Number: 84
Rarity: Ultra Rare
Japanese Price: $25–$35

 Blaine's Doduo 

Set: Gym Leaders 2
Evolution: Into Dodrio
Pokémon Number: 84
Rarity: Common
Japanese Price: $.50–$1

 Koga's Grimer 

Set: Gym Leaders 2
Evolution: Into Muk
Pokémon Number: 88
Rarity: Common
Japanese Price: $.50–$1

 Koga's Muk 

Set: Gym Leaders 2
Evolution: From Grimer
Pokémon Number: 89
Rarity: Rare
Japanese Price: $8–$12

 Sabrina's Gastly 

Set: Gym Leaders 2
Evolution: Into Haunter
Pokémon Number: 92
Rarity: Uncommon
Japanese Price: $2.50–$5

 Sabrina's Haunter 

Set: Gym Leaders 2
Evolution: From Gastly/Into Gengar
Pokémon Number: 93
Rarity: Uncommon
Japanese Price: $2.50–$5

 Sabrina's Gengar 

Set: Gym Leaders 2
Evolution: From Haunter
Pokémon Number: 94
Rarity: Rare (Holofoil)
Japanese Price: $12–$16

 Sabrina's Drowzee 

Set: Gym Leaders 2
Evolution: Into Hypno
Pokémon Number: 96
Rarity: Common
Japanese Price: $.50–$1

Sabrina's Hypno

Set: Gym Leaders 2
Evolution: From Drowzee
Pokémon Number: 97
Rarity: Uncommon
Japanese Price: $2.50–$5

Koga's Koffing (level 10)

Set: Gym Leaders 2
Evolution: Into Weezing
Pokémon Number: 109
Rarity: Common
Japanese Price: $.50–$1

Koga's Koffing (level 15)

Set: Gym Leaders 2
Evolution: Into Weezing
Pokémon Number: 109
Rarity: Uncommon
Japanese Price: $2.50–$5

Koga's Weezing

Set: Gym Leaders 2
Evolution: From Koffing
Pokémon Number: 110
Rarity: Uncommon
Japanese Price: $2.50–$5

Blaine's Rhyhorn

Set: Gym Leaders 2
Evolution: Into Rhydon
Pokémon Number: 111
Rarity: Common
Japanese Price: $.50–$1

[Your] Chansey

Set: Gym Leaders 2
Evolution: None
Pokémon Number: 113
Rarity: Rare
Japanese Price: $6–$10

Koga's Tangela

Set: Gym Leaders 2
Evolution: None
Pokémon Number: 114
Rarity: Common
Japanese Price: $.50–$1

Blaine's Kangaskhan

Set: Gym Leaders 2
Evolution: None
Pokémon Number: 115
Rarity: Uncommon
Japanese Price: $2.50–$5

This pokémon is all about armor. Its basic attack is weak and only works half the time; its advanced attack is good but requires three energy—not great for offense. You do want it for defense though—80 hit points for a basic pokémon is great.

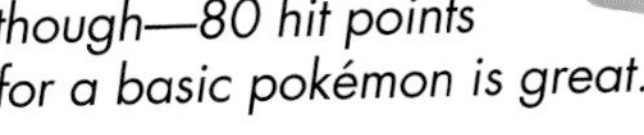

Sabrina's Mr. Mime

Set: Gym Leaders 2
Evolution: None
Pokémon Number: 122
Rarity: Common
Japanese Price: $.50–$1

Sabrina's Jynx

Set: Gym Leaders 2
Evolution: None
Pokémon Number: 124
Rarity: Uncommon
Japanese Price: $2.50–$5

Blaine's Magmar

Set: Gym Leaders 2
Evolution: None
Pokémon Number: 126
Rarity: Uncommon
Japanese Price: $2.50–$5

Giovanni's Pinsir

Set: Gym Leaders 2
Evolution: None
Pokémon Number: 127
Rarity: Rare
Japanese Price: $8–$12

Blaine's Tauros

Set: Gym Leaders 2
Evolution: None
Pokémon Number: 128
Rarity: Common
Japanese Price: $.50–$1

Giovanni's Magikarp

Set: Gym Leaders 2
Evolution: Into Gyarados
Pokémon Number: 129
Rarity: Common
Japanese Price: $.50–$1

This is one of the worst cards in the Basic set, but it gets better in Gym Leaders 2. Its first attack costs one energy and can be attempted once, but if you flip heads you'll dish out 40 damage and 80 damage to pokémon with weakness to water. Ouch!

Giovanni's Gyarados

Set: Gym Leaders 2
Evolution: From Magikarp
Pokémon Number: 130
Rarity: Rare (Holofoil)
Japanese Price: $15–$25

Koga's Ditto

Set: Gym Leaders 2
Evolution: None
Pokémon Number: 132
Rarity: Rare (Holofoil)
Japanese Price: $13–$18

Sabrina's Porygon

Set: Gym Leaders 2
Evolution: None
Pokémon Number: 137
Rarity: Common
Japanese Price: $.50–$1

Team Rocket's Snorlax

Set: Gym Leaders 2
Evolution: None
Pokémon Number: 143
Rarity: Rare
Japanese Price: $10–$15

Still the biggest pokémon in the world, the Gym Leaders 2 version of Snorlax is also still up to its same old trick—sleeping. But sleeping is not a particularly good way of fighting, and Snorlax's abilities bear this out. Twenty damage for three energy and a weak special power means you won't see this sleepyhead in competitive play.

Team Rocket's Zapdos

Set: Gym Leaders 2
Evolution: None
Pokémon Number: 145
Rarity: Rare (Holofoil)
Japanese Price: $16–$24

Blaine's Moltres

Set: Gym Leaders 2
Evolution: None
Pokémon Number: 146
Rarity: Rare (Holofoil)
Japanese Price:$14–$20

Team Rocket's Mewtwo

Set: Gym Leaders 2
Evolution: None
Pokémon Number: 150
Rarity: Rare (Holofoil)
Japanese Price: $16–$24

Team Rocket's version of the rarest of all pokémon was the star of Pokéman: The First Movie. *It is the only basic pokémon that has three different attacks. The first of these allows it to swap damage counters with whatever it is facing for just one energy. Be very careful when battling this thing.*

Trainer Cards

Exchange Discards

Set: Gym Leaders 2
Rarity: Common
Japanese Price: $.50–$1

Gurentown Gym

Set: Gym Leaders 2
Rarity: Uncommon
Japanese Price: $2.50–$5

Invisible Wall

Set: Gym Leaders 2
Rarity: Common
Japanese Price: $.50–$1

Blaine

Set: Gym Leaders 2
Rarity: Rare
Japanese Price: $8–$10

Blaine's Gamble

Set: Gym Leaders 2
Rarity: Common
Japanese Price: $.50–$1

Blaine's Last Resort

Set: Gym Leaders 2
Rarity: Uncommon
Japanese Price: $2.50–$5

Blaine's Test #3

Set: Gym Leaders 2
Rarity: Uncommon
Japanese Price: $2.50–$5

Koga

Set: Gym Leaders 2
Rarity: Rare
Japanese Price: $8–$10

Koga's Secret Transformation

Set: Gym Leaders 2
Rarity: Uncommon
Japanese Price: $2.50–$5

Sabrina

Set: Gym Leaders 2
Rarity: Rare
Japanese Price: $8–$10

Sabrina's ESP

Set: Gym Leaders 2
Rarity: Uncommon
Japanese Price: $2.50–$5

Sabrina's Eye

Set: Gym Leaders 2
Rarity: Common
Japanese Price: $.50–$1

Sabrina's Mental Control

Set: Gym Leaders 2
Rarity: Uncommon
Japanese Price: $.50–$1

Rocket Teammate

Set: Gym Leaders 2
Rarity: Uncommon
Japanese Price: $2.50–$5

Giovanni

Set: Gym Leaders 2
Rarity: Rare
Japanese Price: $8–$10

Giovanni's Last Resort

Set: Gym Leaders 2
Rarity: Rare
Japanese Price: $4–$8

Sekichiku City Gym

Set: Gym Leaders 2
Rarity: Uncommon
Japanese Price: $2.50–$5

Team Rocket Experiment

Set: Gym Leaders 2
Rarity: Uncommon
Japanese Price: $2.50–$5

Team Rocket's Exploding Gym

Set: Gym Leaders 2
Rarity: Uncommon
Japanese Price: $2.50–$5

Tickle Machine

Set: Gym Leaders 2
Rarity: Uncommon
Japanese Price: $2.50–$5

Tokiwa City Gym

Set: Gym Leaders 2
Rarity: Rare
Japanese Price: $5–$10

Warp Point

Set: Gym Leaders 2
Rarity: Common
Japanese Price: $.50–$1

Yamabuki City Gym

Set: Gym Leaders 2
Rarity: Uncommon
Japanese Price: $2.50–$5

Promotional Cards

E3 Pikachu

Set: Promo
Pokémon Level: 12
English Price: $5–$7
This Pikachu was given out at the Electronic Entertainment Expo (E3), a convention for professionals in the computer and video gaming industries. It's the same card as the Pikachu in the Basic set, but it has a small E3 foil stamp below the picture. After the show (May 1999), it was inserted into *Nintendo Power* magazine's September 1999 issue.

Pikachu

Set: Promo
Pokémon Level: 14
English Price: $5–$7
This is the same Pikachu as in the Jungle expansion except it has a W foil-stamped below the picture. This card was inserted into Wizards of the Coast's magazine *The Duelist* (September 1999 issue).

Aerodactyl

Set: Promo
Pokemon Level: 28
English Price: $18-$22
This is the same as the holofoil found in Fossil, except the word "Prerelease" is stamped on the picture. This card was released through the Pokemon League late in October 1999 to anyone playing in the first tournament after Fossil was released.

Pikachu

Set: Promo
Pokémon Level: 16
English 1st Edition Price: $30–$40
English 2nd Edition Price: $18–$24
This card has a small nonfoil star symbol with the word "Promo" printed below the picture. The second edition of this card was initially released in Japan as one of two promotional insert cards in *Hyper Coro Coro* magazine's May (Spring) edition. After that, the first edition appeared in a few random U.S. Jungle booster packs. This was a collation error, and it's unknown how many boosters were affected. Later, Wizards of the Coast's Pokémon Player's League gave out these cards, mostly the second edition versions.

Clefable

Set: Promo
Pokémon Level: 34
English Price: $20–$28
This is a normal Jungle Clefable holofoil with the word "Prerelease" stamped directly on the artwork. It was given out at a few test sites for Wizards of the Coast's Pokémon Player's League.

Jigglypuff

Set: Promo
Pokémon Level: 14
English Price: $40–$50
This is a nonfoil card with a small star symbol and the word "Promo" printed below the picture. This is the other promotional insert card in *Hyper Coro Coro* magazine's May 1999 edition (see Pikachu for the first). This card has not been released in the United States but will likely be a future promotion for the Pokémon Player's League. Note that the value will drop a lot once this happens.

Kabuto

Set: Promo
Pokémon Level: 9
English Price: $3–$5
This is the same Kabuto as in the Fossil expansion except that a sideways foil W and shooting star graphic have been stamped below the picture, directly under the expansion symbol. This card was inserted into the first issue of Wizards of the Coast's card game magazine *Top Deck* (December 1999).

Dragonite

Set: Promo
English Price: $7–$10
Everyone who bought a ticket to *Pokémon: The First Movie* received one of these four cards: Dragonite, Electabuzz, Mewtwo, or Pikachu. They were also given out at Warner Bros. stores with certain purchases.

Electabuzz

Set: Promo
English Price: $7–$10

Mewtwo

Set: Promo
English Price: $8–$12

Pikachu

Set: Promo
English Price: $7–$10

Pokémon by Pokémon Number

1. Bulbasar
2. Ivysaur
3. Venusaur
4. Charmander
5. Charmeleon
6. Charizard
7. Squirtle
8. Wartortle
9. Blastoise
10. Caterpie
11. Metapod
12. Butterfree
13. Weedle
14. Kakuna
15. Beedrill
16. Pidgey
17. Pidgeotto
18. Pidgeot
19. Rattata
20. Raticate
21. Spearow
22. Fearow
23. Ekans
24. Arbok
25. Pikachu
26. Raichu
27. Sandshrew
28. Sandslash
29. Nidoran (Female)
30. Nidorina
31. Nidoqueen
32. Nidoran (Male)
33. Nidorino
34. Nidoking
35. Clefairy
36. Clefable
37. Vulpix
38. Ninetales
39. Jigglypuff
40. Wigglytuff
41. Zubat
42. Golbat
43. Oddish
44. Gloom
45. Vileplume
46. Paras
47. Parasect
48. Venonat
49. Venomoth
50. Diglett
51. Dugtrio
52. Meowth
53. Persian
54. Psyduck
55. Golduck
56. Mankey
57. Primeape
58. Growlithe
59. Arcanine
60. Poliwag
61. Poliwhirl
62. Poliwrath
63. Abra
64. Kadabra
65. Alakazam
66. Machop
67. Machoke
68. Machamp
69. Bellsprout
70. Weepinbell
71. Victreebel
72. Tentacool
73. Tentacruel
74. Geodude
75. Graveler
76. Golem
77. Ponyta
78. Rapidash
79. Slowpoke
80. Slowbro
81. Magnemite
82. Magneton
83. Farfetch'd
84. Doduo
85. Dodrio
86. Seel
87. Dewgong
88. Grimer
89. Muk
90. Shellder
91. Cloyster
92. Gastly
93. Haunter
94. Gengar
95. Onix
96. Drowzee
97. Hypno
98. Krabby
99. Kingler
100. Voltorb
101. Electrode
102. Exeggcute
103. Exeggutor
104. Cubone
105. Marowak
106. Hitmonlee
107. Hitmonchan
108. Lickitung
109. Koffing
110. Weezing
111. Rhyhorn
112. Rhydon
113. Chansey
114. Tangela
115. Kangaskhan
116. Horsea
117. Seadra
118. Goldeen
119. Seaking
120. Staryu
121. Starmie
122. Mr. Mime
123. Scyther
124. Jynx
125. Electabuzz
126. Magmar
127. Pinsir
128. Tauros
129. Magikarp
130. Gyarados
131. Lapras
132. Ditto
133. Eevee
134. Vaporeon
135. Jolteon
136. Flareon
137. Porygon
138. Omanyte
139. Omanstar
140. Kabuto
141. Kabutops
142. Aerodactyl
143. Snorlax
144. Articuno
145. Zapdos
146. Moltres
147. Dratini
148. Dragonair
149. Dragonite
150. Mewtwo
151. Mew

New Pokémon
These were introduced in a Tropical Islands set when *Pokémon: The First Movie* came out in Japan.

Pikablu
Togepi
King Slowpoke
Lady-Ba